The Importance of
Antibonding Orbitals

THE IMPORTANCE

OF ANTIBONDING

ORBITALS

Milton Orchin and H. H. Jaffé
Professors of Chemistry
University of Cincinnati

HOUGHTON MIFFLIN COMPANY · BOSTON
New York · Atlanta · Geneva, Ill. · Dallas · Palo Alto

Note: Figures 5.5, 5.8, 5.10, and 5.11 are reprinted by permission of the Editor of the Journal American Chemical Society. Figures 2.1, 2.2, 4.1, and 4.8 are reprinted by permission of John Wiley and Sons.

Preface

The popularity of molecular orbital theory and its introduction into the chemical curriculum at increasingly early levels have posed many teaching-learning problems. From the molecular orbital point of view, the concept of antibonding orbitals should properly be introduced as early as the description of the bonding in the first row homonuclear diatomics, N_2, O_2, and F_2. The molecular structure of these molecules not only involves electron occupation of σ and π bonding orbitals, but electrons in these compounds occupy antibonding orbitals as well. But a discussion of such orbitals at this level is seldom pursued beyond the mention of the practice of affixing an asterisk to σ and π to denote the antibonding character of these σ^* and π^* orbitals.

Antibonding orbitals are characterized by having a node perpendicular to the bond axis. On the other hand, bonding orbitals have no such node and thus have positive overlap between bonded atoms. Consequently, electrons occupying antibonding orbitals not only add nothing to the bonding energy of a molecule, but actually subtract from it.

Most reactions in the ground state can be described without involving antibonding orbitals and hence a consideration of these orbitals is not forced into the discussion. Also, there are frequently more conventional if not equally satisfactory ways of explaining certain phenomena. Thus, for example, adding electrons to the system $K_3Co(CN)_6$ in which Co^{3+} has a d^6 configuration would require that the filled 18 electron stable system around Co ($6 + 6 \times 2 = 18$) be expanded. In molecular orbital terminology the addition of an electron would require occupation of a high energy antibonding e_g^* orbital. Both the familiar "octet" rule and the molecular orbital theory correctly predict the instability of the system produced by adding an electron to the closed shell configuration.

However, advances in chemistry are such that explicit discussion of antibonding orbitals is now desirable at an early level. We hope therefore to convince teachers, students, and mature practicing chemists of the value of understanding antibonding orbitals by demonstrating their importance. Of course such orbitals cannot be discussed without reference to bonding and non-bonding orbitals and electron distribution problems in general. In this context our title is a bit of a gimmick, but such dramatization does focus attention where we wish it.

In this book we attempt first to give an adequate (but far from complete or rigorous) background required to understand some principles of molecular orbital theory. We then proceed to a discussion of the first row diatomic molecules, concluding with a consideration of the structure of carbon monoxide. Building on this background, we next discuss some of the metal carbonyls since these compounds offer rich examples for our theme: that the structure and properties of many molecules as well as their reactions are more satisfactorily understood when the availability and participation of antibonding orbitals is considered.

In many molecules some antibonding orbitals are occupied in the ground state. To excite further electrons into antibonding orbitals requires substantial amounts of energy. Thus the energy-rich systems resulting from absorption of ultraviolet radiation (ultraviolet absorption spectroscopy) and reactions of molecules in the excited state (photochemistry) involve occupation of antibonding orbitals. Chapter 4 is devoted to this topic.

In photochemically excited states, not only are antibonding orbitals almost invariably occupied, but such occupation frequently determines the path of the reaction. The Hoffmann-Woodward rules, discussed in Chapter 5, are a particularly elegant example of this use of antibonding orbitals.

Our choice of examples is of course arbitrary, partly governed by our current interests, partly by our desire to be brief, partly by the desire to make our material comprehensible to the second year college student. Our task has not been the elucidation of new principles or theories but the pedagogical one of integration, systemization, and, we hope, stimulation. An overdose is frequently fatal to an effort with such goals. Finally, we hope our book will be read with at least a fraction of the pleasure we had in writing it.

Acknowledgments: We wish to thank Professors M. S. Newman and Jack Calvert for arranging a Visiting Professorship at Ohio State University for one of us (MO) which facilitated the writing of a portion of the book. We are especially grateful to Nelson F. Phelan for the preparation and editing of the drawings and for carefully reading and discussing the entire manuscript, but most important for giving us the benefit of fresh illumination of subject matter by a perceptive and creative student. Finally, we wish to thank Mrs. Marcella Barton for valuable and expert stenographic assistance.

MO
HHJ

Cincinnati, Ohio

Contents

1

Atomic and Molecular Orbital Theory

1.1 ATOMIC ORBITAL THEORY

The beginning of modern atomic orbital theory is associated with the Bohr* theory of the hydrogen atom, proposed in 1913. Bohr suggested that the electron of the hydrogen atom travels in a circular orbit around the nucleus, held fixed in its path by the balancing of the centrifugal force of the revolving electron against the force of attraction between the negatively charged electron and the positive nucleus. This concept of the rotating electron is the so-called planetary theory of the atom. Bohr further assumed that only certain electron orbits were permitted, the radii of these orbits being determined by a so-called quantum number n which is an integer; i.e., $n = 1, 2, 3, \cdots$, etc. The most stable electronic state of the hydrogen atom (the ground state) is that in which the electron is in the orbit with the lowest quantum number, $n = 1$. If the hydrogen atom is exposed to a source of great energy, the electron may be promoted to the

* Niels Bohr was born in 1885 in Copenhagen and was educated at the University there, receiving a Ph.D. in 1911. Upon graduation he studied under Sir J. J. Thompson at the Cavendish Laboratory of the University of Cambridge, and then in 1912 moved to Manchester where he worked under Sir Ernest Rutherford. In 1916 he was appointed Professor of Theoretical Physics at Copenhagen and in 1920 became Head of the Institute of Theoretical Physics there. In the years 1913–1915 he published three papers which contained theoretical explanations of Balmer's formula for the hydrogen spectrum. He was awarded the Nobel Prize for Physics in 1922 at the age of 37. As Director of the Institute of Theoretical Physics he ordered all work halted when the Nazis invaded Denmark and he subsequently fled to England. When Bohr died in 1962 he was universally acknowledged as one of the great physicists of all time.

orbit in which $n = 2$. If the energy source is light energy, the frequency of the light absorbed is proportional to the energy required to excite the electron from the $n = 1$ to the $n = 2$ level, and the resulting hydrogen atom is said to be in the first excited state. The frequency, ν(nu), the number of waves passing a given point per second, of the light absorbed is related to the energy by the fundamental equation for all emission or absorption spectroscopy: $E = h\nu$ where h is a constant, called Planck's constant after Max Planck. This universal equation was deduced by Planck* and Einstein.† The frequency of light required for the promotion of an electron from $n = 1$ to $n = 2$ in the hydrogen atom can be calculated to be 2.4675×10^{15} cycles/sec. The frequency is related to the wave number $\tilde{\nu}$ (nu, tilde) (the number of waves per centimeter), by the equation

$$\tilde{\nu} = \nu/c \text{ where } c \text{ is the velocity of light } (3 \times 10^{10} \text{ cm/sec})$$

Accordingly the above frequency corresponds to $82,251$ cm^{-1} or $10^8/82,251 = 1216$ Ångstroms (A) or 121.6 mμ. Light at this wavelength corresponds to about 235 kcal/mole and such light is present on the sun.

---

* Max Planck was born in Kiel, Germany, on April 23, 1858, and was educated at Munich. He became an Assistant at Munich University and was subsequently appointed a Professor in Kiel in 1885 and in Berlin in 1889. His radiation law was first published in 1901; later Planck extended the quantum theory to all kinds of energies and added the information that both emission and absorption proceed discontinuously, i.e., that energy is quantized. In 1918 Planck was awarded the Nobel Prize for Physics, and in 1926 was elected a foreign member of the Royal Society. He died in 1947.

† Albert Einstein was born May 14, 1879, at Ulm, Germany. He spent his early boyhood in Munich and then in Milan, Italy. At fifteen Einstein began attending school in Aarau, Switzerland, and eventually became a Swiss citizen. He became a patent examiner at Berne in 1900, and in 1905, while working there, announced his theory of relativity. He took his Ph.D. at the University of Zurich where he became Professor of Physics in 1909. In 1911, he became Professor of Physics in Prague but returned to Zurich the following year. In 1913 he became Director of the Kaiser-Wilhelm Institute for Physics in Berlin and was named Professor at the University of Berlin in 1914. In 1921 he received the Nobel Prize in Physics for his work on relativity. Einstein was in the U.S.A. in 1933, when he was stripped of his honorary German citizenship by the Nazis. He then became a member of the Institute for Advanced Study in Princeton where he spent the rest of his life. He became an American citizen in 1940. One of his earlier publications gives complete theory and formulae of Brownian motion, but he soon became interested in quantum theory. He developed the Law of the Photoelectric Effect as a consequence of this interest. In 1950 he published his unified field theory. Einstein died in 1955, the world's best known and most admired scientist.

The simple planetary theory of atomic structure failed to explain certain features of the observed spectra of atoms with more than one electron, and it became necessary to modify the Bohr theory. The first significant modification was suggested by Arnold Sommerfeld,* who proposed that the planetary orbits of electrons were elliptical rather than circular. In order to define the elliptical orbit, a second quantum number was required, relating to the eccentricity of the ellipse. In modern theory, this second quantum number is called l, the *azimuthal* quantum number, in contrast to the *principal* quantum number n. l can take all integral values between 0 and $n - 1$. Each l specifies one of the subshells: $l = 0$ is s, $l = 1$ is p, $l = 2$ is d, etc.

In 1924 the young French Physicist, Louis de Broglie,† suggested that very small particles, such as electrons, could travel in waves; i.e., that small particles can exhibit wave as well as particle properties. Some typical wave properties are wavelength, frequency, and interference phenomena; particle properties are those of mass, energy, and momentum. For light a similar duality between wave and particle behavior was well established by the work of Planck and Einstein, and de Broglie suggested that the same is true for electrons: For some purposes it is convenient, or even necessary, to express electron properties in terms of a particle and for others it is convenient to describe the electron behavior in terms of waves.

Various kinds of waves, such as sound waves, the waves generated by a plucked string on a guitar, etc., can be described in terms of wave equations; and electron waves can also be

---

* Arnold Sommerfeld was born in December, 1868, in East Prussia. In 1891 he received his Ph.D. degree from Königsberg University in Mathematical Physics. He then went to Göttingen University and then to the Mining Academy in Clausthal. From there he moved to Aachen, and then in 1906 accepted the chair of Theoretical Physics at Munich where he succeeded Ludwig Boltzmann. He died in April, 1951.

† Prince Louis de Broglie was born August 15, 1892, in Dieppe, France. He studied at the Lycée Janson-de-Sailly and received a baccalauréat in history in 1909 from the Sorbonne. He obtained a license in science from the same school in 1913. During World War I de Broglie was assigned to the radio-telegraph branch of the French Corps of Engineers. In 1919 he studied physics in his brother's laboratory and received a Ph.D. at the Sorbonne in 1924. In 1929 he received the Nobel Prize in Physics for his contributions to the theory of the wave nature of the electron, first published in 1924. In 1928 de Broglie was appointed Professor of Theoretical Physics at the Henri Poincaré Institute of the University of Paris, and he is permanent Secretary of the Académie des Sciences.

described by similar wave equations. Electron waves resemble the standing waves generated by imparting motion to a piece of string held in the hand at one end and fixed to an object at the other end. Such waves, shown in Fig. 1.1, are characterized by possessing motion such that the amplitude of the wave regularly reaches a maximum in one direction and alternately the amplitude periodically reaches a minimum in the same plane in the opposite direction; half way between the maximum and minimum, the amplitude is zero. These zero amplitude positions are called nodes and the direction, or sign of the wave, changes on passing through a node. Thus, the amplitude of the wave is a function of the distance along the wave. The wave described above moves only in one plane, and the amplitude is a function of only one coordinate. Electron waves can, of course, move in all planes and hence the amplitude, or wavefunction — frequently designated as ϕ (phi) — is a function of three coordinates, indicated as $\phi(x, y, z)$. In all wave equations, the square of the wave function is the property which has physical significance. In the case of the electronic wavefunction $\phi(x, y, z)$, the square of this function represents the probability of finding the electron in the volume element of space, $dx\, dy\, dz$.

After de Broglie proposed that electrons may have wave properties, it remained for Schrödinger,* Heisenberg,† and Dirac** in the period 1926–1928 to develop the formalisms by

* Erwin Schrödinger was born August 12, 1887, in Vienna. His elementary education was private, and in 1898 he entered the Akademische Gymnasium. In 1906 he started his studies at the University of Vienna under Hasenlohr. In 1920 he accepted a junior post with Max Wien in Jena and four months later moved to Stuttgart. Subsequently, he accepted professorships in Kiel, Vienna, and Breslau. He then went to Zurich for six years and afterwards to Berlin. In 1933 he left Germany for Oxford and in the same year shared the Nobel Prize with Dirac. In 1938 he accepted a professorship at Graz, but after Hitler's invasion of Austria, he fled to Rome. He then went to Ireland and became a professor at the Dublin Institute for Advanced Study. In 1957 he was offered a chair at Vienna and died there on January 4, 1961.

† Werner Heisenberg was born in Germany in 1901 and was educated at Munich and Göttingen. He became Professor of Physics at Leipzig in 1927 and was awarded the Nobel Prize in Physics in 1932. He is best known for his "Uncertainty Principle" which states that when an electron is in motion, its position and its velocity cannot be simultaneously precisely ascertained.

** Paul A. M. Dirac was born in August, 1902, in Bristol, England. He received a degree in Electrical Engineering in 1921, and did his Ph.D. work at Cambridge, where he received the Ph.D. degree in 1926. In 1932 he became Professor of Mathematics at Cambridge University. He shared the 1933 Nobel Prize in Physics with Schrödinger.

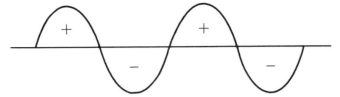

FIGURE 1.1 • A Typical Wave.

which this concept could be translated into an effective treatment of real problems. Schrödinger's formalism is the simplest and most convenient for molecular problems. He developed basic equations which connect the energy of an electronic system with its wave function. Although it is only possible to solve the wave equation exactly for the most simple systems, approximate solutions have proved nevertheless to be very fruitful. The wavefunctions that are solutions to the wave equations are called orbitals, and thus orbitals are wavefunctions.

There are three types of orbitals that are of interest to us for the purpose of this book: the so-called s, p, and d orbitals. The s orbitals are characterized by being spherically symmetrical around the nucleus, or positive center, of the atom. It is common practice to represent the s orbital by a circle. The circle in turn represents a cut of a sphere, and the sphere is a probability sphere in which the probability of finding the electron in this spherical volume is related to the distance of the electron from the nucleus. Thus, for example, for the hydrogen atom a sphere with a radius of 1.7A represents a probability of .95 of finding the electron at a distance of 1.7A or less from the nucleus — i.e., there is a 19:1 chance that the electron of the hydrogen atom is within a sphere of radius 1.7A around the nucleus. The familiar circle can be drawn to any size at the convenience of the author, thus implying an arbitrary scale of distance from the nucleus and an arbitrary probability. The circle tells us the shape of the s orbital and further tells us that there is a high probability of finding the electron within a sphere represented by the circle. Although the s orbital has no node, the p orbital has one node and the d orbitals two nodes; the shape of these orbitals are indicated in Fig. 1.2.

There is always a good deal of confusion about what exactly these shapes represent. If we wish to represent probability surfaces, then we are really dealing with ϕ^2 and not ϕ; and hence we cannot put a plus sign on one lobe and a minus sign on

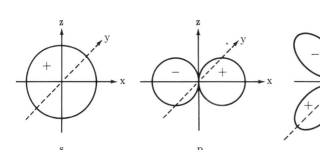

FIGURE 1.2 • s, p, and d Orbitals.

another because ϕ^2 is positive everywhere. The p orbital or wavefunction is correctly drawn as two equal circles touching at one point with a positive sign in one lobe and a negative sign in the other lobe. The probability surface for this wavefunction, ϕ^2, is dumbbell shaped, and there is no difference in sign in the two lobes. As commonly used, the concepts are mixed; the probability surface, ϕ^2, is usually shown, but the wavefunction (ϕ) is implied by the difference in sign of the two lobes in the p orbital.

1.2 THE PERIODIC CLASSIFICATION

In building the periodic chart of the elements, three principles are observed. The first of these is the "aufbau" or building-up principle which states that electrons are put into orbitals in order of the energy of the orbital; the lowest energy orbitals are filled first before electrons are placed in higher energy orbitals. The order of orbital energy is well established as $1s < 2s < 2p < 3s < 3p < 4s < 3d$ . . ... The second principle is the Pauli* exclusion principle which states that a maximum of two electrons can occupy an orbital and then only providing that the spins of the electrons are paired or opposed. The third

---

*Wolfgang Pauli was born on April 25, 1900, in Vienna. In 1918 he became a student of Sommerfeld at the University of Munich and received his Ph.D. in 1921. He went to the University of Göttingen and in 1922 to Niels Bohr's Institute at Copenhagen. In 1923 he was appointed Privat-docent at the University of Hamburg and remained there until 1928 when he went to the Eidgenössische Technische Hochschule in Zurich, where he was affiliated at the time of his death in 1958. He spent 1940–1945 at the Institute for Advanced Study in Princeton, and in 1945 was awarded the Nobel Prize for his work on the exclusion principle.

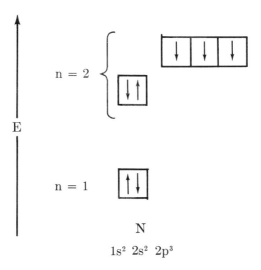

FIGURE 1.3 • The Electronic Configuration of the Nitrogen Atom.

principle is Hund's* rule which states that one electron is placed in all orbitals of equal energy (*degenerate* orbitals) before two electrons are placed in any one of the degenerate set and the electrons in the singly occupied orbitals have parallel spins. The three rules can be illustrated by considering the atomic structure of the nitrogen atom, $1s^2 2s^2 2p^3$, as shown in Fig. 1.3.

1.3 MOLECULAR ORBITAL THEORY — BONDING AND ANTIBONDING ORBITALS. THE HYDROGEN MOLECULE.

As two individual hydrogen atoms at quite a large distance from each other are (theoretically) brought closer and closer together, eventually the nucleus of each atom will start to attract the electron originally associated solely with the other atom. The change in energy of the system as a function of

* G. Friederich Hund was born February 4, 1896, at Karlsruhe. He was Professor of Theoretical Physics at Leipzig (1929–1946), Professor of Mathematical Physics at Jena (1946–1951), Professor at Frankfurt am Main (1951–1956), and has been Professor of Theoretical Physics at Göttingen since 1956. In 1943 he received the Max Planck Prize and in 1949 the National Prize of the German Democratic Republic.

distance is usually shown in the form of a curve called a Morse*
curve (Fig. 1.4). When the distance separating the nuclei is at
or near the bonding distance, the two electrons in the system
are both associated with the two nuclei; and instead of the
original atomic orbital on each atom, we now have a *molecular
orbital* which results from the combination of atomic orbitals.
When one electron is near one nucleus, the molecular orbital
(or wavefunction) may be assumed to resemble the atomic
orbital (or wavefunction, ϕ_A) of that atom. Similarly, when the
electron is in the neighborhood of the other nucleus, the molecular orbital (MO) resembles ϕ_B. Since the complete MO has
characteristics separately possessed by ϕ_A and ϕ_B, it is approximated as a *linear combination* (linear combinations are those
made by simple addition or subtraction of the functions to be
combined) of the atomic orbitals. In this above case we can
indicate the molecular orbital (ψ) formed by the addition of
the two atomic orbitals as: $\psi_b = \phi_A + \phi_B$. This terminology,
called the linear combination of atomic orbitals or LCAO

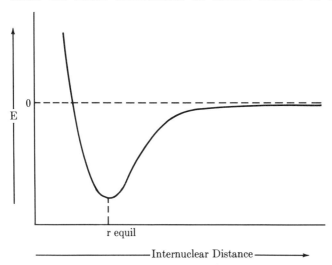

FIGURE 1.4 • The Morse Curve for the Hydrogen Molecule.

* Philip M. Morse was born in 1903 in Shreveport, Louisiana. He was
raised in Cleveland, Ohio, and attended the Case Institute of Technology
where he received his B.S. degree in 1926. He did his graduate work at
Princeton University under Karl T. Compton, receiving his Ph.D. in 1929.
He remained at Princeton for a year and then moved to the Massachusetts
Institute of Technology, where he became Professor in 1937. In 1946 he
went to the Brookhaven National Laboratories as Director, but resigned
in 1948 and returned to M.I.T. as Professor of Physics.

method, was first suggested by R. S. Mulliken.*

The addition of the two AO's represented by the ψ_b MO implies that the two electrons in the hydrogen molecule are now shared by, or interact with, both nuclei; i.e., the MO is bicentric. The addition further implies that both electrons will spend most of their time between the two nuclei and hence help to bond the two hydrogen atoms together. Thus the subscript b on ψ_b indicates that the MO is *bonding*, and the orbital is referred to as a *bonding orbital*.

The process of adding the two AO's together may be represented graphically in several ways. One simple way is to consider the boundary surface of the MO as made from the overlap of the two boundary surfaces of the individual AO's (Fig. 1.5).

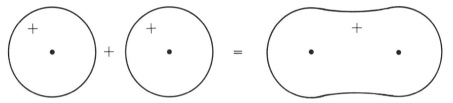

FIGURE 1.5 • The Addition of Two 1s Atomic Orbitals.

The $+$ sign in the MO indicates that the wavefunction is positive everywhere and consequently there is no node. Again it must be borne in mind that the sign of a probability surface curve has no meaning. However, we will continue to use dual notation of showing probability boundaries (ϕ^2 or ψ^2) with algebraic signs to indicate wavefunctions (ϕ or ψ) because of the importance of the nodal properties.

* Robert S. Mulliken was born June 7, 1896, at Newburyport, Massachusetts. He received a B.S. degree from M.I.T. in 1917 and a Ph.D. in physical chemistry from the University of Chicago in 1921. In 1917–1918 he was Junior Chemical Engineer at the Bureau of Mines. Dr. Mulliken was employed by the New Jersey Zinc Company from 1919 to 1921 and subsequently became a Fellow of the National Research Council. He was named Assistant Professor of Physics at N.Y.U. in 1926, Associate Professor of Physics at the University of Chicago in 1928, and full Professor there in 1931. In 1957 he was named Ernest DeWitt Burton Distinguished Service Professor. He has received awards from American and British scientific societies, and was the recipient in 1966 of the Nobel Prize in chemistry. His special interests are separation of isotopes, theory of molecular spectra, diatomic molecules, and the electronic structures of molecules. He retired in 1961, and now spends summers at the University of Chicago, and winters at Florida State University working at the Institute of Molecular Biophysics, of which another distinguished spectroscopist, Michael Kasha (cf footnote p. 65), is director.

In the linear combination explained above, we added the two separate AO's. It can be shown by quantum mechanical arguments that the LCAO method applied to diatomics requires that a second MO be generated from the AO's by another linear combination of AO's. In general, the LCAO of k atomic orbitals must generate k molecular orbitals. A rationalization of the necessity of two MO's from two AO's can be made as follows: Each atomic orbital can accommodate a maximum of two electrons; if two atomic orbitals combine, the combination must result in generating a sufficient number (two) of molecular orbitals to accommodate a maximum of four electrons.

The second linear combination of hydrogen AO's can be obtained by subtracting one AO from the other, viz. $\psi_a = \phi_A - \phi_B$. We can represent this process by the boundary surface procedure as shown in Fig. 1.6. In this MO the probability of finding

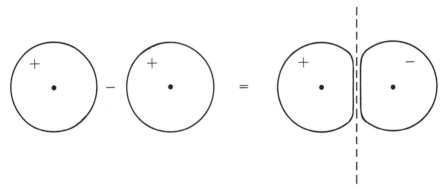

FIGURE 1.6 • The Subtraction of Two 1s Atomic Orbitals.

the electrons at exactly half the distance between the nuclei is zero; i.e., there is a nodal plane in the MO, shown as a dashed line in Fig. 1.6. On the average, electrons in ψ_a are farther from either of the nuclei than they would be in the isolated atoms, and hence the atoms would be in an energetically more favorable condition if they were separated than if they were close together. Because electrons in such an orbital would tend to separate the atoms, the orbital (or wavefunction) is called an *antibonding* orbital; hence the subscript a in ψ_a.

We saw above that the LCAO method applied to two hydrogen atomic orbitals, ϕ_A and ϕ_B, led to two MO's, ψ_a and ψ_b. We can represent this process by an energy diagram (Fig. 1.7). The horizontal lines at the edges of the diagram represent the

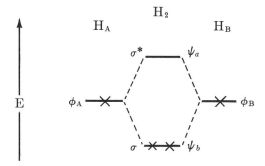

FIGURE 1.7 • The Molecular Orbital Energy Diagram for H_2.

(equal) energy of each atomic orbital; the levels* in the middle represent the energies of the bonding and antibonding MO's.

1.4 SIGMA AND SIGMA STARRED ORBITALS

The boundary surface of $\psi_b = \phi_A + \phi_B$ is shown in Fig. 1.5, and the plus sign inside this surface indicates that the orbital is plus everywhere; i.e., there is no node. It is very desirable to describe a bond between two atoms in terms of the symmetry of the orbital occupied by the electrons bonding the atoms together. Specifically, a description of the symmetry of the orbital with respect to the bond axis is desired. If we were to take the egg-shaped orbital of Fig. 1.5 and rotate it around the internuclear axis, say by an angle of 180° (or any angle for that matter), the resulting shape would be indistinguishable from the original. We have performed a symmetry operation. Furthermore, since the orbital was plus everywhere, the rotation has not affected the sign of the orbital anywhere — all the plus parts (which in this case were everywhere) have been transformed under the symmetry operation into plus parts. When a symmetry operation is performed and the resulting orbital has the same signs everywhere as the original, we say the orbital is *symmetric* with respect to that operation. In the present example, ψ_b is symmetric with respect to rotation around the internuclear axis. Because this property characterizes the s atomic orbital, we call the molecular orbital, which is symmetric

---

* In a common approximation (neglect of the so-called overlap integral), it is found that the energy of the antibonding orbital lies as much above the isolated atomic orbital as the energy of the bonding orbital lies below it.

with respect to rotation around the internuclear axis, a σ (sigma, Greek equivalent of s) molecular orbital.

Now let us examine the antibonding orbital ψ_a pictured in Fig. 1.6. We see that, with respect to rotation around the internuclear axis, this orbital is also symmetric. Although the orbital has two equal halves of different signs, the signs do not change on rotation around the axis joining the centers of each half. Accordingly, this orbital is also a sigma orbital. However, it is desirable to distinguish this higher energy sigma orbital ψ_a from the lower energy sigma orbital ψ_b.

Whereas the orbital ψ_b was positive near both atoms A and B, ψ_a is characterized by opposite signs near the two atoms, and consequently a node between them. To emphasize that both orbitals are sigma orbitals, they are both commonly denoted by σ instead of ψ; to emphasize the antibonding nature of ψ_a it is customary to add an asterisk: σ^*.

If the atoms A and B are like atoms, the distinction between σ and σ^* can be reduced to a *symmetry* distinction. If we assume a mirror halfway between A and B, we see that the *shapes* of both σ and σ^* are unchanged by reflection in the mirror. But the sign of σ is unchanged, i.e., it is *symmetric* with respect to this reflection. On the other hand, the sign of σ^* is reversed, $+$ replaced by $-$ and *vice versa*, and hence σ^* is called *anti-symmetric* with respect to reflection in the plane.

1.5 THE NON-EXISTENT HELIUM MOLECULE

Having developed the molecular orbitals from the combination of the 1s orbitals, ϕ_A and ϕ_B, of the two hydrogen atoms in the hydrogen molecule, we placed the two electrons of H_2 in ψ_b of Fig. 1.7. Now suppose we wish to indicate the molecular orbital energy diagram of two combined helium atoms. Each He atom has two electrons in 1s orbitals, and so the combination of He_2 has four electrons. The combination of the 1s orbitals of the two helium atoms leads to the same orbital energy diagram (Fig. 1.7.) as in hydrogen, but we now place two of the four electrons into ψ_b, and, according to the Aufbau and Pauli principles, we must place the remaining two in the σ^* orbital ψ_a. In the common approximation of neglect of overlap integrals (see Chapter 2), the bonding and antibonding levels are evenly spaced below and above the isolated atomic level so that equal electron occupation of the two levels results in exact cancellation of the bonding effect of σ by the antibonding effect of σ^*. The net result is that He_2 is not a stable species; as a matter of fact, in a somewhat less crude approximation, if the overlap integral (S) is not neglected, the antibonding orbital is more antibonding than the bonding orbital is bonding, and hence He_2 is unstable.*

1.6 PI AND PI-STARRED ORBITALS

In the above discussion we have considered the combination of two s orbitals to form σ and σ^* orbitals. Let us now turn our attention to the combination of two p orbitals. We again make our linear combination by the addition and subtraction of the orbitals (Fig. 1.8). The original atomic p orbitals each have one node; the resulting $\psi_b = \phi'_A + \phi'_B$ has one node, but $\psi_a = \phi'_A - \phi'_B$, where the ϕ' are the 2p atomic orbitals, has two nodes. The new node now appears between the two nuclei and hence the orbital is antibonding. Because both molecular orbitals have the same nodal properties as the p orbital, we call ψ_b a π (pi, Greek equivalent of p) orbital and ψ_a a π^* (pi-starred) orbital.

In considering the symmetry properties of the σ and σ^* orbitals (Figs. 1.5 and 1.6, respectively), we pointed out that both were symmetric with respect to rotation around the internuclear axis. We see that with respect to the same symmetry operation, π and π^* are both antisymmetric; and this property is what distinguishes the π orbitals from the σ orbitals.

Just as with the σ and σ^*, π does not have a node but π^* does have a node *between* the atoms. Again, if the atoms are alike,

---

* The energies of the two orbitals including overlap are expressed by the equations:

$$E_{\psi_b} = E_\phi + \frac{\beta - SE_\phi}{1 + S} \qquad E_{\psi_a} = E_\phi - \frac{\beta - SE_\phi}{1 - S}$$

Here, E_ϕ is the energy of the electron in an atomic orbital ϕ_A (or ϕ_B) of an isolated hydrogen atom; and $(\beta - SE_\phi)/(1 \pm S)$ is the splitting of ψ_b and ψ_a from this level, as shown in Fig. 1.7. β represents an integral, called the *resonance integral*, which measures the interaction of two atomic orbitals and is often assumed proportional to S. Since $\beta - SE_\phi$ is a negative quantity, $(\beta - SE_\phi)/(1 + S)$, the stabilization of the bonding orbital, is less than $(\beta - SE_\phi)/(1 - S)$, the destabilization of the antibonding orbital.

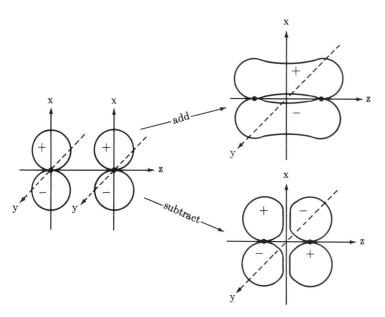

FIGURE 1.8 • The Addition and Subtraction of 2p Atomic Orbitals.

π is symmetric, and π^* is antisymmetric with respect to a mirror plane between the atoms. At this point we can introduce a third type of symmetry operation besides the rotation around an axis and reflection from a mirror.

This operation, *inversion*, consists of inverting every part of a molecule or orbital by taking a point anywhere in the orbital, drawing a line from it through the center of the molecule, and continuing an equal distance in the same direction. If at this new point, a point of equal magnitude to the old one, the sign of the orbital is identical with that of the original point, the orbital is symmetric with respect to inversion;* if the new point has an opposite sign, the orbital is antisymmetric with respect to inversion. The German words *gerade* (even) and *ungerade* (uneven) are frequently used to denote the symmetric and anti-symmetric behavior respectively with respect to inversion. Thus we can call the π orbital *u* (*ungerade*) and the π^* orbital *g* (*gerade*). The *g* and *u* are frequently used as subscripts. Reference to Figs. 1.5, 1.6, and 1.8 shows that, if A and B are like atoms,

---

* We postponed discussion of this operation to this point because, in considering σ orbitals, it could not have been distinguished from reflection at a mirror plane.

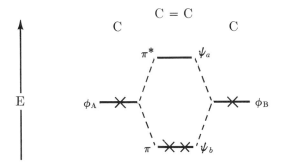

FIGURE 1.9 • The Molecular Orbital Energy Diagram for the Inter-action of Two 2p Atomic Orbitals.

we have σ_g, σ_u^*, π_u, and π_g^* orbitals.

The energy diagram for the combination of two p atomic orbitals can be written analogously to that of the combination of two s atomic orbitals (Fig. 1.9). Again, the splitting in the neglect-of-overlap-integral-approximation can be written as equal; i.e., the antibonding orbital is as much antibonding as the bonding orbital is bonding. This level diagram would describe correctly the π-system in ethylene (Fig. 1.10). In the ground or normal state the two π electrons are paired and in the lowest energy orbital ψ_b. If the ethylene molecule is subjected to just the right amount of light energy, i.e., if it is excited, an electron in ψ_b will be promoted to ψ_a in what is called a $\pi \rightarrow \pi^*$ (pi to pi-starred) transition. The energy difference (or vertical distance in Fig. 1.9) between ψ_b and ψ_a in ethylene is considerably less than the analogous energy difference between ψ_b and ψ_a in the hydrogen molecule; accordingly, we find that ethylene absorbs at about 185 mμ, corresponding

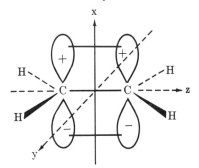

FIGURE 1.10 • The Structure of Ethylene.

to an energy of about 155 kcal/mole. In the above excited electronic configuration, one electron remains in ψ_b and the other electron is now in ψ_a, or the electronic configuration of this excited state may be written $\pi\pi^*$ or $\pi_u\pi_g^*$. In the same system of notation, the ground state is expressed as π^2 or π_u^2. We are now in a position to consider the electronic structure of some simple diatomic molecules, and we will discover that, even in the ground or normal state, electrons can and do occupy antibonding orbitals.

2

The Structure of Some Diatomic Molecules

Before proceeding to examine the molecular structure of some simple diatomic molecules, we will find it useful to examine two concepts which are basic to a more complete molecular orbital treatment, namely normalization and orthogonality.

2.1 NORMALIZATION

Although we can never know where to find a small particle like an electron at any particular moment, we can determine the probability of finding it in any given region in space. The position of the electron can be defined by a probability function. This function is usually called ρ (rho), and is proportional to the square of the wavefunction (ϕ^2 or ψ^2) discussed in Chapter 1. The electron is most likely to be found in those regions of space where ρ is largest. If we define a small volume of space in terms of infinitesimal distances along three axes, $dx\ dy\ dz = d\tau$ (de tau), then $\rho d\tau$ is the probability of finding the electron in the small volume $d\tau$. Now since the electron must be found somewhere in space, if we integrate the probability from plus infinity to minus infinity, i.e., over all space, we should get unity:*

$$\int_{-\infty}^{+\infty} \int_{-\infty}^{+\infty} \int_{-\infty}^{+\infty} \rho\ dx\ dy\ dz = \int \rho\ d\tau = \int (N\phi')^2\ d\tau = 1$$

where N is the proportionality constant. When the last equality is satisfied, the wavefunction is said to be normalized; i.e., when

---

* For simplicity, whenever we write the integral symbol, $\int$, with the differential $d\tau$, we mean integration over all space, i.e., from $-\infty$ to $+\infty$ for x, y, and z.

17

the square of the wavefunction integrated over all space is equal to unity, the wavefunction is normalized. For the purposes of our discussion here, atomic orbitals, which we have called ϕ, all include the normalization factor N and are therefore already normalized so that $\int \phi^2 \, d\tau = 1$.

In the last chapter we saw how the combination of two atomic orbitals, e.g., the atomic orbitals or wavefunctions of two hydrogen atoms, H_A and H_B, combined to form two molecular orbitals:

$$\psi_b(\sigma_g) = \phi_A + \phi_B \quad \text{and} \quad \psi_a(\sigma_u^*) = \phi_A - \phi_B$$

These molecular wavefunctions are not normalized and must now be normalized, i.e., multiplied by a factor N such that $\int (N\psi)^2 \, d\tau = 1$. In order to do so we write for ψ_b:

$$\int [N(\phi_A + \phi_B)]^2 \, d\tau = 1 \quad \text{or} \quad N^2 \int (\phi_A + \phi_B)^2 \, d\tau = 1$$

$$N^2 \int (\phi_A^2 + 2\phi_A\phi_B + \phi_B^2) \, d\tau = 1$$

or $\qquad N^2[\int \phi_A^2 \, d\tau + 2\int \phi_A\phi_B \, d\tau + \int \phi_B^2 \, d\tau] = 1$

Since the atomic orbitals ϕ_A and ϕ_B are already normalized, $\int \phi_A^2 \, d\tau = 1 = \int \phi_B^2 \, d\tau$. The third integral, $\int \phi_A\phi_B \, d\tau$, is called the overlap integral and is given the symbol S. The overlap integral is a measure of the extent of overlap of the atomic orbitals ϕ_A and ϕ_B and the numerical value of S varies from zero to positive (or negative) unity. In ethylene, for example, the overlap integral for the $2p\pi$ orbitals is about 0.3. If in the above equation we replace the overlap integral by the symbol S, we have

$$N^2[2 + 2S] = 1 \text{ or } 2N^2[1 + S] = 1 \text{ and } N = \pm 1/\sqrt{2(1 + S)}.$$

Since we usually want our wavefunctions positive, we take the plus sign and drop the minus sign; however, this choice is arbitrary and immaterial. In much work in molecular quantum mechanics, the very crude approximation $S = 0$ (see footnotes, pp. 11 and 13) is made. In that case, the last equation becomes $N = +1/\sqrt{2}$ and the full wavefunction for the bonding molecular orbital of the hydrogen molecule is then

$$\psi_b = \frac{1}{\sqrt{2}} \phi_A + \frac{1}{\sqrt{2}} \phi_B$$

The constants $1/\sqrt{2}$ are called coefficients, c; and they tell us to what extent each atomic orbital is participating in the molecular orbital. The above wavefunction is a specific example of the generalized wavefunction:

$$\psi = c_1\phi_1 + c_2\phi_2 + \cdots$$

and in terms of these coefficients our requirement for normalization is (assuming $S = 0$)

$$\Sigma c^2 = c_1{}^2 + c_2{}^2 + \cdots = 1$$

And checking our bonding wavefunction for the hydrogen molecule to verify the normalization condition:

$$\left(\frac{1}{\sqrt{2}}\right)^2 + \left(\frac{1}{\sqrt{2}}\right)^2 = 1$$

If the same procedure is carried out for the antibonding wavefunction, one should obtain:

$$\psi_a = \frac{1}{\sqrt{2}}\phi_A - \frac{1}{\sqrt{2}}\phi_B$$

2.2 ORTHOGONALITY

According to quantum mechanics, any two molecular wavefunctions, in order to be proper wavefunctions of the same system, must be orthogonal to one another. The mathematical condition for orthogonality is: the product of the two wavefunctions, integrated over all space, must be equal to zero: $\int \psi_1\psi_2 \, d\tau = 0$. Let us take the two molecular wavefunctions for the hydrogen molecule and test their orthogonality:

$$\int \psi_b\psi_a \, d\tau = \int \left(\frac{1}{\sqrt{2}}\phi_A + \frac{1}{\sqrt{2}}\phi_B\right)\left(\frac{1}{\sqrt{2}}\phi_A - \frac{1}{\sqrt{2}}\phi_B\right) d\tau$$

$$= \int \left(\frac{1}{2}\phi_A{}^2 - \frac{1}{2}\phi_B{}^2\right) d\tau = \frac{1}{2}\int \phi_A{}^2 \, d\tau - \frac{1}{2}\int \phi_B{}^2 \, d\tau$$

and since $\qquad \int \phi_A{}^2 \, d\tau = \int \phi_B{}^2 \, d\tau = 1$

we have $\qquad \int \psi_b\psi_a \, d\tau = \dfrac{1}{2} - \dfrac{1}{2} = 0$

Perhaps a graphical representation will make the concept clearer. If we represent the separate atomic orbitals of the two

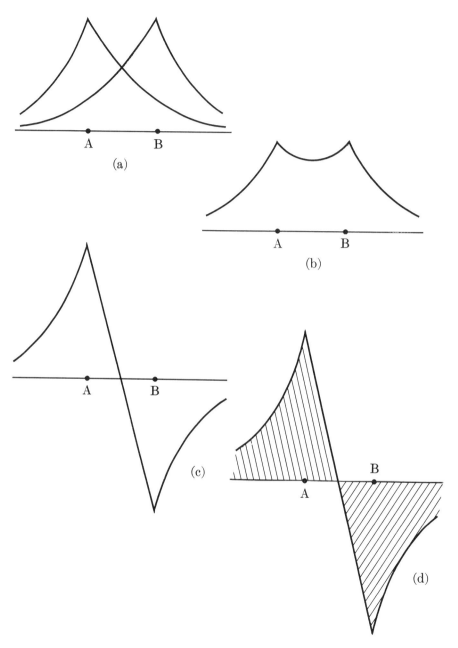

FIGURE 2.1 • Atomic and Molecular Orbital Wavefunctions Plotted Against Internuclear Distance. (a) ϕ_A and ϕ_B; (b) $\psi_b = \phi_A + \phi_B$; (c) $\psi_a = \phi_A - \phi_B$; (d) $\psi_b\psi_a = (\phi_A + \phi_B)$ $(\phi_A - \phi_B)$.

separate hydrogen atoms in Fig. 2.1a, the graphical representation of the molecular orbitals ψ_b and ψ_a (Figs. 2.1b and 2.1c) follows from the addition and subtraction, respectively, of the two atomic orbitals shown in Fig. 2.1a. The product of ψ_b and ψ_a is graphically represented in Fig. 2.1d. We see that the area under the curve of the left half (which is positive) is exactly equal to the area under the right half of the curve (which is negative), and hence the net area under the curve (the integral of the product) is exactly zero.

Finally, it should be mentioned that wavefunctions which are both orthogonal and normalized are frequently called *orthonormal* functions.

2.3 HOMONUCLEAR DIATOMICS OF THE FIRST ROW ELEMENTS

2.31 THE STRUCTURE OF NITROGEN

The electronic configuration of the nitrogen atom is $1s^2 2s^2 2p^3$ (Fig. 1.3). When two nitrogen atoms combine, the same orbital types combine if they are of equal or approximately equal energy. Thus, the 1s, 2s, $2p_x$, $2p_y$, $2p_z$ orbitals on one nitrogen combine with the similar orbitals on the other nitrogen to give, in each case, two molecular orbitals. The five atomic orbitals on each atom give rise to ten molecular orbitals in the molecule. Because each atom contributes seven electrons, the total of 14 electrons in the molecule will distribute themselves in seven of the ten molecular orbitals. Since the electrons will occupy the orbitals in order of increasing energy, we must arrange our molecular orbitals in an energy sequence so that we may place our 14 electrons properly. One of the most instructive ways to do this is by means of the molecular orbital energy diagram method (Fig. 2.2). We have already discussed the combination of two s orbitals to give σ and σ^* MO's. In the nitrogen molecule we have the combination of both 1s and 2s orbitals to give the four σ type orbitals, two bonding and two antibonding, all of them occupied by two electrons each. Because the 1s electrons are not valence electrons, we usually pay little heed to them. The combination of the 2s orbitals does not result in any net bonding and these electrons can be crudely identified with the lone pair on each nitrogen in the familiar valence bond method

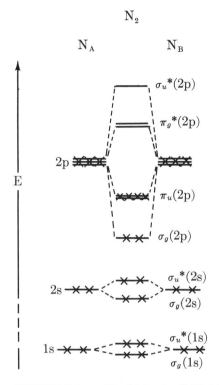

FIGURE 2.2 • The Molecular Orbital Energy Diagram for N_2, Unhybridized.

of writing nitrogen as :N≡N:. Another way of representing the fact that the 2s orbitals do not interact appreciably is to show relatively little splitting in the MO level diagram; i.e.,

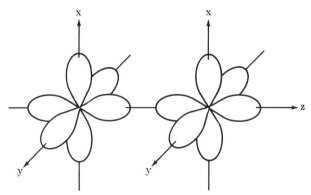

FIGURE 2.3 • Customary Orientation of the 2p Orbitals.

the distance of $\sigma_g(2s)$ and $\sigma_u^*(2s)$ from the isolated atomic 2s level is not very large.

The three atomic p levels in the isolated atom are of equal energy (degenerate); but when we bring one atom into the field of the other (cf. Fig. 2.3), the p_z orbitals pointing toward the other atom start to interact to form a σ bond between the two atoms (see Fig. 2.4a). Of course, the corresponding σ^* orbital must also be generated (Fig. 2.4b). The orbitals $\sigma_g(2p_z)$ and $\sigma_u^*(2p_z)$, although generated from the combination of atomic $2p_z$ orbitals, are in fact σ molecular orbitals because they are symmetric with respect to rotation around the internuclear axis (the z axis of Fig. 2.3). The bonding interaction is quite large and hence the splitting is quite large.

The p_x and p_y orbitals on each nitrogen (Fig. 2.3) combine to

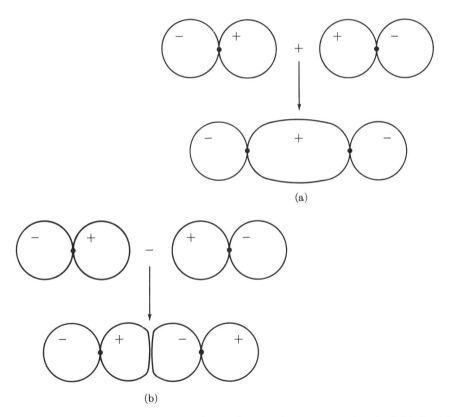

(a)

(b)

FIGURE 2.4 • Formation of the Sigma Orbitals from the $2p_z$ Atomic Orbitals. (a) $\sigma_g(2p)$; (b) $\sigma_u^*(2p)$.

each form a π set: $\pi_u(2p_x)$, $\pi_g^*(2p_x)$; $\pi_u(2p_y)$, $\pi_g^*(2p_y)$. The form of these orbitals has been shown in Fig. 1.8. The p_x and p_y orbitals are perpendicular (orthogonal) to each other and the $\pi_u(2p_x)$ and $\pi_u(2p_y)$ orbitals are therefore also perpendicular to each other as must be $\pi_g^*(2p_x)$ and $\pi_g^*(2p_y)$ (see Fig. 2.5). Now if we refer back to our level diagram, we see that there are suffi-cient electrons to occupy completely the $\pi_u(2p_x)$ and $\pi_u(2p_y)$ orbitals but that the $\pi_g^*(2p_x)$ and $\pi_g^*(2p_y)$ as well as the $\sigma_u^*(2p_z)$ are unoccupied. The net bonding between the nitrogen atoms then comes from the $\sigma_g(2p_z)$ and the $\pi_u(2p_x)$ and $\pi_u(2p_y)$ bond-ing molecular orbitals as any bonding contribution from $\sigma_g(1s)$ and $\sigma_g(2s)$ is cancelled by the corresponding antibonding con-tribution from $\sigma_u^*(1s)$ and $\sigma_u^*(2s)$.

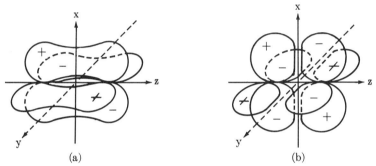

(a)   (b)

FIGURE 2.5 • The Pi Molecular Orbitals of the Nitrogen Molecule. (a) $\pi_u(2p)$; (b) $\pi_g^*(2p)$.

2.32 THE STRUCTURE OF OXYGEN

The valence electrons of oxygen are in the 2s and 2p orbitals with the configuration $2s^2 2p^4$. The molecular orbital energy diagram would be essentially that constructed for nitrogen (Fig. 2.2), as we are using the same set of atomic orbitals in our combinations (the same basis set). However, it is now neces-sary that the molecular orbitals accommodate 16 electrons of which 12 (all 2s and 2p electrons) are referred to as valence electrons. If we follow the principles used for the periodic classification, the two electrons which must be added to the nitrogen (ten valence electrons) system must go separately into the $\pi_g^*(2p_x)$ and $\pi_g^*(2p_y)$ orbitals, with spins parallel (Hund's rule). The two unpaired electrons in the π^* orbitals give rise to the paramagnetic properties of molecular oxygen. (Mole-cules or atoms with one or more unpaired electrons are attracted by an external magnetic field and hence are said to be para-magnetic.) The diradical character of oxygen is perhaps its most outstanding physical property.

The occupation of antibonding orbitals by one or more elec-trons cancels some of the bonding attraction between the atoms. In the O_2 example, we have two π bonding orbitals, each doubly occupied, and a σ bonding orbital, doubly occupied, or a total of three bonding orbitals. However, each of the two electrons in the antibonding orbitals cancels the bonding effect of an electron in a bonding orbital. Thus the net bonding in oxygen can be considered to result from a double bond, (since two elec-trons constitute a bond, 6 bonding electrons -2 antibonding electrons $= 4$ net bonding electrons, or $4/2 = 2$ bonds). Evi-dence for the effect of occupation of the antibonding orbitals comes from bond distances. In the ground or normal state, the bond distance between oxygen atoms is 1.2074A. However, when O_2 is ionized (i.e., if an electron were lost from one of the π_g^* antibonding orbitals) the resulting $O_2{}^+$ species should have a stronger interaction between the two oxygen atoms. In fact, the bond distance of $O_2{}^+$ is 1.1227A, a considerable decrease, indicative of stronger bonding in the ion. The $O_2{}^+$ species is very interesting. It not only carries a positive charge, but it also has one unpaired electron; it is properly called a radical-cation.

2.33 THE STRUCTURE OF FLUORINE

The molecular level diagram of F_2, which contains two F atoms each with the valence configuration of $2s^2 2p^5$, is basically that of the other second row homonuclear diatomics and differs from O_2 in that two additional electrons must be accommodated. These two additional electrons will go into the $\pi_g^*(2p_x)$ and $\pi_g^*(2p_y)$ orbitals of Fig. 2.2. Now two antibonding π^* orbitals are completely filled and this antibonding character cancels the bonding generated from two π bonding orbitals. The net bond-ing thus results from the σ bond p_z interaction between the atoms. This fact is apparent in the conventional valence bond structure of $F_2 \left(:\overset{..}{\underset{..}{F}}:\overset{..}{\underset{..}{F}}: \right)$. The three lone pair electrons on each fluorine atom are associated with the canceling effect of $\sigma_g(2s) - \sigma_u^*(2s)$; $\pi_u(2p_x) - \pi_g^*(2p_x)$; and $\pi_u(2p_y) - \pi_g^*(2p_y)$. Since the antibonding cancels the bonding, the net result in each interaction is to have a lone pair on each atom corresponding to the three bonding-antibonding interactions.

The effect of increasing occupancy of antibonding orbitals is dramatically illustrated by the decreasing bond energies of N_2, O_2, and F_2, which are: 225, 118, and 36 kcal/mole, respectively. Thus it is over six times more difficult to dissociate N_2 than F_2 into its atoms. Furthermore, the bond distances increase in the expected order: $1.10A(N_2)$; $1.21A(O_2)$ and $1.42A(F_2)$.

2.4 HYBRIDIZATION

In discussing the molecular orbital energy diagram for the nitrogen molecule, it will be recalled that we combined the 2s orbitals on each atom to generate $\sigma_g(2s)$ and $\sigma_u^*(2s)$ molecular orbitals, weakly bonding and weakly antibonding respectively. We then combined the $2p_z$ orbital on each nitrogen to form the strongly bonding $\sigma_g(2p_z)$ and the strongly antibonding $\sigma_g^*(2p_z)$ MO's.

This picture of the nitrogen molecule (Fig. 2.2) is not completely adequate. Much more extensive calculations show that the highest occupied molecular orbital is a σ_g orbital and this result has been verified experimentally. The simplest way to reconcile our naive picture with these findings comes from a recognition that the σ_g orbitals and the σ_u^* orbitals are not as simple as we had visualized them; they are not each formed from only 2s or $2p_z$ atomic orbitals. We can take care of this shortcoming in several ways.

When any two orbitals are of the same type (say σ_g), they can interact with one another. According to the rules of quantum mechanics, this interaction *always* lowers the lower one and raises the higher one of the pair. Accordingly the mixing of $\sigma_g(2s)$ and $\sigma_g(2p_z)$, and of $\sigma_u^*(2s)$ and $\sigma_u^*(2p_z)$ depresses $\sigma_g(2s)$ and $\sigma_u^*(2s)$ and raises $\sigma_g(2p_z)$ and $\sigma_u^*(2p_z)$, as shown in Fig. 2.6. It must then be true that $\sigma_g(2p_z)$ has been raised sufficiently to end up above $\pi_u(2p)$, so that it becomes the highest occupied orbital.

Unfortunately the interactions discussed in the preceding paragraphs obscure the essential nature of the process. By interacting $\sigma_g(2s)$ and $\sigma_g(2p_z)$ we have in effect mixed 2s and $2p_z$ orbitals. This was possible because, relative to the *molecule*, they have the same symmetry properties, i.e., the s and p

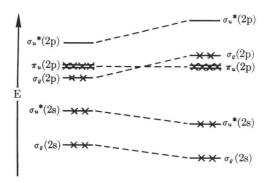

FIGURE 2.6 • Spreading of Energies of Orbitals of the Same Type.

orbitals on the isolated atom are g and u respectively, whereas with respect to the molecule both of these orbitals are g. The mixing of the 2s and $2p_z$ orbitals on the same atom is a favorable process because, as Linus Pauling* pointed out, the *hybrid* orbitals which result have much better bonding properties than the pure 2s or 2p orbitals. Without hybridization, the combination of orbitals were as follows: $2s_A$ and $2s_B$ combine to give:

$$\sigma_g(2s) = N_1(\phi_{2s_A} + \phi_{2s_B})$$

$$\sigma_u^*(2s) = N_2(\phi_{2s_A} - \phi_{2s_B})$$

and the $2p_{z_A}$ and $2p_{z_B}$ combine to give:

$$\sigma_g(2p_z) = N_3(\phi_{2p_A} + \phi_{2p_B})$$

$$\sigma_u^*(2p_z) = N_4(\phi_{2p_A} - \phi_{2p_B})$$

With hybridization we first mix the 2s and 2p orbitals on each atom before we combine the orbitals of different atoms. Thus the hybrid orbitals are atomic orbitals insofar as they are re-

* Dr. Linus Pauling was born in Portland, Oregon, on February 28, 1901. He did his undergraduate work at Oregon State College and received his Ph.D. from the California Institute of Technology in 1925. He officially joined that Institute's teaching staff in 1922 and his entire career up until 1964 was spent there. He was Chairman of the Division of Chemistry and Chemical Engineering and Director of the Gates and Crellin Laboratories of Chemistry. Dr. Pauling received the Nobel Prize in Chemistry in 1954 and the Nobel Peace Prize in 1962, and thus is the only person in history to be the sole possessor of two Nobel Prizes. Dr. Pauling has probably contributed more than any other chemist to the understanding of chemical phenomena, and there is hardly any area of chemistry his genius has not touched. In 1964 Dr. Pauling retired from the California Institute of Technology and took a position with the staff of the Center for Study of Democratic Institutions.

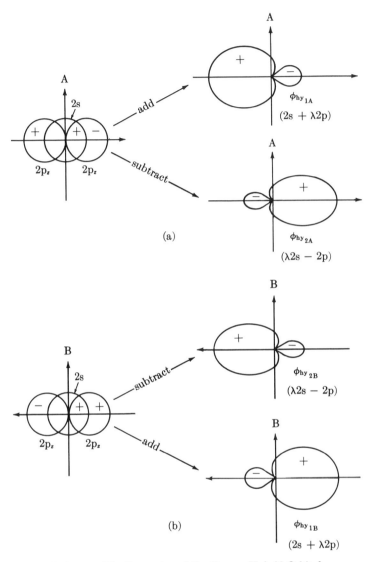

FIGURE 2.7 • The Formation of the Two sp Hybrid Orbitals.

stricted to a single atom and do not encompass the entire molecule. If we mix the 2s and $2p_z$ orbitals on one nitrogen atom we obtain:

$$\phi_{hy_1} = N_5(\phi_{2s} + \lambda\phi_{2p_z})$$

$$\phi_{hy_2} = N_6(\lambda\phi_{2s} - \phi_{2p_z})$$

where the N's are normalization constants and the λ is a weighting factor. The weighting factor would be unnecessary if the hybrid orbitals were made up of equal parts of s and p, but one orbital (ϕ_{hy_1}) has *more* s than p character, and the other (ϕ_{hy_2}) *less* s than p, as is seen from the form of the hybrid wavefunctions ($0 \leq \lambda \leq 1$). (The physical picture of the hybridization is represented by Fig. 2.7.) Thus we have obtained two sp hybrid orbitals on each nitrogen atom which are oriented at 180 degrees from one another.

In combining the sp hybrids of two different nitrogen atoms (A and B), we want to use that set of hybrids which will give the best bond: in this case the hybrids (ϕ_{hy_2}) with the greater p character. Combining the ϕ_{hy_2} of the two nitrogen atoms to obtain molecular orbitals:

$$\sigma_g = N_7(\phi_{hy_{2A}} + \phi_{hy_{2B}})$$

$$\sigma_u^* = N_8(\phi_{hy_{2A}} - \phi_{hy_{2B}})$$

This process is represented in Fig. 2.8. We are left with one

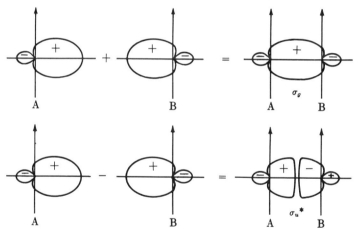

FIGURE 2.8 • Formation of σ_g and σ_u^* Orbitals from the ϕ_{hy_2} sp Hybrid Orbitals.

hybrid orbital (ϕ_{hy_1}) on each nitrogen atom. These hybrids, however, are oriented so that they are pointing away from each other and hence their interaction is quite small. Combining the ϕ_{hy_1} of the two different nitrogen atoms we obtain:

$$\sigma_g = N_9(\phi_{hy_{1A}} + \phi_{hy_{1B}})$$

$$\sigma_u^* = N_{10}(\phi_{hy_{1A}} - \phi_{hy_{1B}})$$

This is represented by Fig. 2.9.

The resulting molecular orbital diagram is pictured schematically in Fig. 2.10. We know that this cannot be the com-

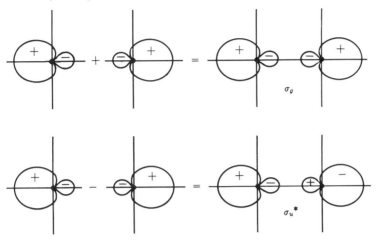

FIGURE 2.9 • Formation of σ_g and σ_u^* Orbitals from the ϕ_{hy_1} sp Hybrid Orbitals.

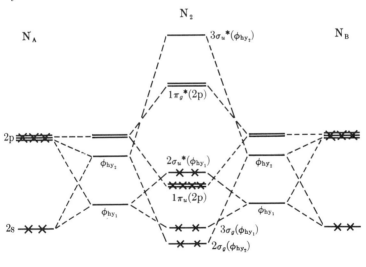

FIGURE 2.10 • Simplified Molecular Orbital Energy Diagram for N_2, including Hybridization.

pletely correct diagram as the highest occupied orbital in this diagram is a $\sigma_u(2\sigma_u^*)$, and not a σ_g as experimentally observed. To obtain the final correct molecular orbital diagram we recall that any two orbitals of the same type (say σ_g) can interact with one another. Concentrating on the σ_g and σ_u orbitals* of Fig. 2.10, as pictured in Fig. 2.11, we see that the σ_g's interact and also that the σ_u's interact. The interaction, as usual, lowers the lower one and raises the higher one of the pair, as shown.

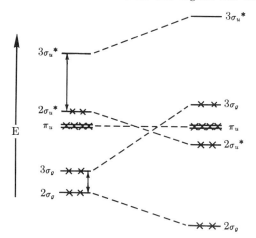

FIGURE 2.11 • Spreading of Energies of Hybrid Orbitals of the Same Type.

The important result here is that the highest occupied orbital has become the correct $\sigma_g(3\sigma_g)$. Incorporating this modification into a complete molecular orbital diagram, we obtain the final and correct ordering of energy levels as shown in Fig. 2.12.

In Fig. 2.10 and 2.12 we have introduced a very common and useful notation, the symbols $2\sigma_g$, $3\sigma_g$, $2\sigma_u^*$, $3\sigma_u^*$ for the new hybrid molecular orbitals. Since we mixed s and p_z orbitals to obtain the hybrids, the resulting molecular orbitals can no longer be identified with specific atomic orbitals and some notation is needed to indicate the difference. The numbers preceding the σ's are order numbers, or pseudoquantum numbers, simply ordering the MO's of the same type in order of increasing energy (i.e., $1\sigma_g$ is of lower energy than $2\sigma_g$, etc.). We extend the notation to all of the MO's of the diagram, even if they can be identified with a specific atomic orbital, for clarity and consistency.

* $1\sigma_g$ and $1\sigma_u^*$ come predominantly from 1s atomic orbitals and therefore do not contribute to any significant extent.

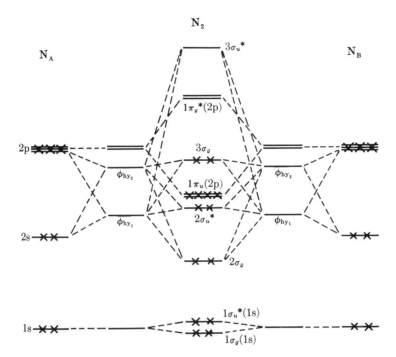

FIGURE 2.12 • The Correct Molecular Orbital Energy Diagram for N_2.

2.5 THE STRUCTURE OF CARBON MONOXIDE

In considering the structure of N_2, O_2, and F_2, we combined the orbitals on two identical atoms in forming the above homonuclear diatomic molecules. We shall now consider the combination of two different atoms of the first row elements. The general problem is to consider the results of the difference in electronegativity of the two different atoms. We know that the nuclear charge increases with increasing atomic number. Since, for first row atoms, the valence electrons are all L shell electrons, and, hence, at about the same distance from the nucleus, it will be increasingly difficult to remove them; i.e., the electrons in the 2s and 2p orbitals decrease in energy as the nuclear charge increases and they are thereby stabilized. In constructing the MO level diagrams, one should place the 2s and 2p orbitals of the more electronegative element (the one with the higher nuclear charge) lower than the corresponding orbitals of its partner.

In constructing the MO level diagram of carbon monoxide (Fig. 2.13) we see that the levels of the isolated oxygen atom are below those of the isolated carbon atom. In making the combination of σ bonding orbitals, we invoke the same general concepts of hybridization as we employed in the case of N_2. In the nitrogen case, the hybrid orbitals on each nitrogen atom were equal in energy. In the carbon monoxide case this is not true. The two hybrid orbitals on oxygen do not match the energies of those on carbon; as a matter of fact, the lower energy sp hybrid on carbon approximately matches the energy of the higher energy hybrid on oxygen, with the result that the two lone pairs of electrons — electrons in the non-bonding orbitals σ_{nb} — are on the lower energy hybrid of oxygen and the higher energy hybrid of carbon. These relationships are shown in Fig. 2.13. (Note that no g and u subscripts occur, since heteronuclear

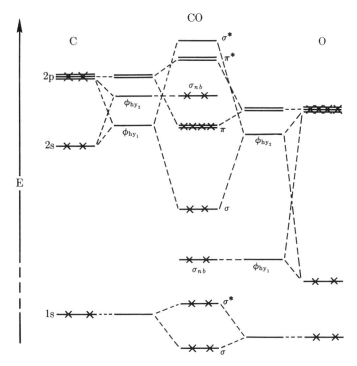

FIGURE 2.13 • The Molecular Orbital Energy Diagram for CO.

diatomic molecules have no center of inversion, and hence the g and u classification is inappropriate.)

There are thus two lone pairs of electrons on carbon monoxide, neither involved substantially in bonding. One pair, as explained above, is on oxygen in a hybrid orbital, mostly s in character, and thus in a very stable (unreactive) orbital. The other lone pair is on the carbon atom and has a high degree of p character. This orbital extends away from the carbon-oxygen bond and is a high energy (loosely bound) orbital. The reactivity of electrons in this orbital accounts for the well-known

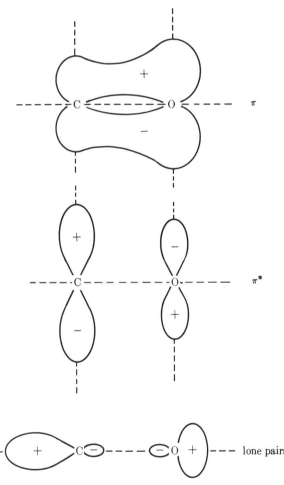

FIGURE 2.14 • Molecular Orbitals of CO. (a) One π Orbital; (b) One π^* Orbital; (c) The Lone Pairs, σ_{nb}.

donor properties of carbon monoxide. The bonding between carbon and oxygen results from the sigma bond, mostly on the oxygen, and the set of π orbitals, π_x, π_y, also mostly on the oxygen atom. The energy diagram shows the π^*'s lying much closer to the carbon p's than to the oxygen p's. The lone pairs on carbon and oxygen and one each π and π^* orbitals are illustrated in Fig. 2.14. The π orbitals are mostly on the oxygen atom since the oxygen atom contributes more to the π than does carbon. The other π bonding MO is at right angles; i.e., in front and behind the paper to the one shown. The antibonding orbitals, π_x^*, in Fig. 2.14 show that the carbon makes a larger contribution to this orbital than does oxygen. There is another π^* orbital, the π_y^*, at right angles to the π_x^* orbital. The shape of the orbitals shown in Fig. 2.14 follows directly from the positions of the MO's relative to the atomic orbitals shown in Fig. 2.13. The fact that the π^* orbitals are close in energy to the carbon p orbital and concentrated on the carbon atom is of very great importance in considering the acceptor properties of CO in a variety of carbonyl complexes.

3

The Structure and Infrared Spectra of Some Carbonyl Complexes

3.1 INTRODUCTION

The fascinating group of metal carbonyl compounds, exemplified by the first one to be discovered,* nickel tetracarbonyl

---

* The discovery of Ni(CO)₄ was announced in 1890 by Ludwig Mond, Carl Langer, and Friedrick Quincke, in the *J. Chem. Soc.*, **57**, 749 (1890). Born in Kassel, Germany, in 1839, Ludwig Mond, after some industrial experience in Germany, emigrated to England in 1862. He subsequently introduced into England the Solvay process for making sodium carbonate (soda ash). In the Solvay process, ammonia and carbon dioxide are passed successively into a saturated solution of sodium chloride. The reaction, $\overline{CO_2} + H_2O \rightleftharpoons H^+ + HCO_3^-$, proceeds to ammonium bicarbonate in the presence of NH₃:

$$\overline{NH_3} + H^+ + HCO_3^- \rightleftharpoons NH_4HCO_3$$

However, when a high concentration of NaCl is present the following occurs:

$$NaCl + NH_4HCO_3 \rightleftharpoons NaHCO_3 + NH_4Cl$$

The precipitated NaHCO₃ is filtered, washed, and gently heated to give soda ash: $2NaHCO_3 \xrightarrow{\Delta} Na_2CO_3 + H_2O + \overline{CO_2}$. In order to make the process more economical, the firm of Brunner, Mond and Company was attempting to obtain chlorine from the NH₄Cl by-product. The corrosive NH₄Cl was vaporized in brick-lined tanks having nickel valves. These valves corroded very badly and investigation revealed that the small amount of CO in the CO₂ gas used for sweeping out the ammonia was the culprit causing the formation of nickel and carbon deposits. Mond described [*J. Soc. Chem. Ind.*, **14**, 945 (1895)] his critical subsequent experiments on the reaction between CO and finely divided Ni as follows:

"In the course of these experiments finely divided nickel, formed by reducing nickel oxide at 400° by hydrogen, was treated with pure CO in a glass tube at varying temperatures for a number of days, and was then cooled down in a current of CO before it was removed from the tube. In order to keep the poisonous CO out of the atmosphere of the laboratory,

Ni(CO)₄, is of interest for a variety of reasons. In the first place the carbonyls have most unusual physical properties, considering that they are derivatives of a metal; while most metallic compounds are high-melting solids, the carbonyls are frequently low-melting liquids and gases; e.g., $Ni(CO)_4$, a tetrahedral compound like CCl_4, is a colorless stable liquid boiling at 42°C. Cobalt tetracarbonyl hydride, $HCo(CO)_4$, also called cobalt hydrocarbonyl, is a gas at room temperature; it melts at about −33° and its boiling point is probably about −12°, although it has never been measured because the pure compound is so unstable. Nevertheless this compound is the active catalyst in the so-called "Oxo" process in which olefins are converted to alcohols; millions of pounds of oxo alcohols are produced in the U.S. yearly in an industry valued at over two billion dollars — all made possible by the unusual reactivity of $HCo(CO)_4$. Many of the metal carbonyls are solid crystalline compounds. Thus when $HCo(CO)_4$ is allowed to decompose under certain conditions, two molecules collide and molecular hydrogen is liberated: $2 HCo(CO)_4 \rightarrow [Co(CO)_4]_2 + H_2$. The other product of the reaction is cobalt tetracarbonyl dimer or dicobalt octacarbonyl, a beautifully crystalline deep orange compound melt-

we simply lit the gas escaping from the apparatus. To our surprise we found that while the apparatus was cooling down, the flame of the escaping gas became luminous and increased in luminosity as the temperature got below 100°. On a cold plate of porcelain put into this luminous flame, metallic spots were deposited similar to the spots of arsenic obtained with a Marsh apparatus; and on heating the tube through which the gas was escaping, we obtained a metallic mirror, while the luminosity disappeared." Condensation of the escaping gas gave the colorless liquid with a musty odor which proved to be Ni(CO)₄.

The attempt to obtain chlorine from NH₄Cl was abandoned. The ammonia value is now reclaimed by heating the NH₄Cl solution with lime, CaO, a by-product from the manufacture of CO_2:

$$CaCO_3 \xrightarrow{\Delta} CaO + \overline{CO_2}$$

$$2NH_4Cl + CaO \rightarrow 2\overline{NH_3} + H_2O + CaCl_2.$$

Thus the only by-product of the Solvay process is $CaCl_2$. Today this chemical is frequently used for melting snow and ice on roads and walks.

Incidentally, the vigor of Mond can be appreciated when it is pointed out that the accidental discovery of Ni(CO)₄ occurred in 1890, and by 1895 an experimental plant in London was refining Ni from Canadian ores, by taking advantage of the volatility of Ni(CO)₄, at the rate of 1½ tons weekly. Ludwig Mond's son, Sir Alfred Mond, later Lord Melchett, although trained in the law, followed in his father's footsteps as a great industrial organizer and became Chairman of Imperial Chemical Industries, the great English chemical concern, as well as serving in Parliament for 17 years. A settlement in Israel, Tel-Mond, is named after him.

ing at about 52°. In dicobalt octacarbonyl there are two metal atoms, but much more complicated carbonyls are known: thus, in one of the rhodium carbonyls, the structure of which was recently proven, there are six metal atoms — $Rh_6(CO)_{16}$ — with each rhodium at the corner of an octahedron.

Not only do the carbonyls have unusual physical properties for compounds containing metal atoms, but the chemical properties are also fascinating. Of fundamental interest is the nature of the bonding between the metal atom and the coordinated carbon monoxide. The nature of the metal-carbon bond has always intrigued chemists: Here is the borderline between organic and inorganic compounds. One need only think of the amazingly versatile Grignard reagent "RMgX" discovered by Victor Grignard* in 1900 to appreciate the interest such compounds have for all chemists.

3.2 THE d ORBITALS

Fundamental to any discussion of transition metal chemistry is the consideration of d orbitals. The fourth row of the periodic table begins with potassium (atomic no. 19); but following Ca(20) the filling of the third octet (the N shell) is interrupted by the filling of the d orbitals in the shell below because of the energy sequence — ... $< 3p < 4s < 3d < 4p$ .... Since there are five 3d orbitals, ten elements occur after Ca (Sc, Ti, V, Cr, Mn, Fe, Co, Ni, Cu, Zn) before the filling of the fourth shell is resumed. The ten elements listed above belong to the first transition metal series. There is a second transition metal series of elements with one to ten 4d electrons and a third series with 5d electrons. Those elements having partly filled d shells are formally defined as transition metals — hence $Zn°$ with a d^{10} configuration is not included as a transition metal.

It will be remembered that s orbitals have no nodes and p orbitals have one node. The d orbitals have two nodes and hence two changes in algebraic sign (4 lobes). The distribution of electron density and the usual identification of the five d

---

* Victor Grignard, *Compt. rend.*, **130**, 1322 (1900). Grignard was born in France in 1871 and died in 1935. He was Professor of Chemistry first at the University of Nancy and later at the University of Lyon where he most appropriately succeeded Barbier who had initiated the work on the use of magnesium in organic syntheses. Grignard was awarded the Nobel Prize in Chemistry in 1912 jointly with his countryman Paul Sabatier, a pioneer in the use of solid catalysts for hydrogenation reactions.

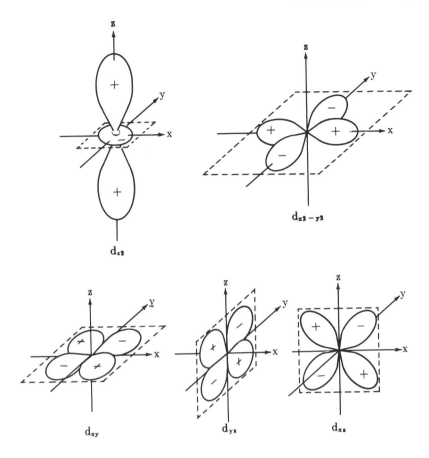

FIGURE 3.1 • The Five d Orbitals.

orbitals are shown in Fig. 3.1. The set of three, d_{xy}, d_{yz}, d_{xz}, are characterized by having the lobes of the orbitals pointing between the coordinate axes indicated in the subscript to d. The $d_{x^2-y^2}$ and d_{z^2} orbitals have lobes pointing along the axes. One might conclude that since there are a set of three orbitals pointing *between* the axes there should be a set of three orbitals pointing *along* the axes. In fact, the d_{z^2} represents a linear combination of $d_{z^2-y^2}$ and $d_{z^2-x^2}$ (Fig. 3.2); in particular, the addition. However, in the d orbital set there can only be a total of five orbitals, just as in the p orbital set there can only be three orbitals. Although it would have been possible to combine any two of the set of three d orbitals pointing along

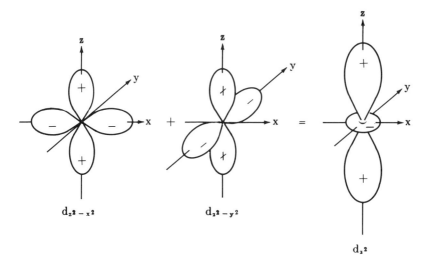

FIGURE 3.2 • Synthesis of the d_{z^2} Orbital.

the axes, the usual combination is the one shown. In this combination (addition) the positive lobes along the z axes of $d_{z^2-x^2}$ and $d_{z^2-y^2}$ add to form the large positive lobe of d_{z^2} along the z axis; the negative lobes along the x axis of $d_{z^2-x^2}$ and along the y axis of $d_{z^2-y^2}$ combine to form a negative doughnut in the xy plane. This orbital is sometimes called the dumbbell-doughnut orbital. The four other d orbitals, for obvious reasons, are referred to as cloverleaf orbitals.

As we mentioned earlier, the first transition metal series is characterized by having one or more electrons, but less than ten, in 3d orbitals. We shall see that this is a crucial requirement in forming stable complexes like the carbonyls.

There are now several hundred known complexes of transition metals which have one or more CO groups present in the molecule; among these are a large number and variety of complexes in which CO is the only ligand present. These latter "pure" carbonyls may be divided into three large classes: the monomeric carbonyls in which only one metal atom is present and all CO's are complexed to the one metal [$Ni(CO)_4$, $Fe(CO)_5$, $W(CO)_6$]; the carbonyls in which several metals may be present and bonded to each other while the CO's are each bonded to only one metal [$(CO)_5Mn—Mn(CO)_5$, $(CO)_4Co—Hg—Co(CO_4)$]; and the carbonyls in which there are CO's which bridge one or more metal atoms:

3.3 THE EFFECTIVE ATOMIC NUMBER (E.A.N.) CONCEPT

The systemization and integration of this large variety of carbonyls is greatly facilitated by the concept of the *Effective Atomic Number* (EAN), i.e., the total number of electrons which enter into the electronic configuration of the central atom. The EAN is usually (but not always) the number of electrons in the configuration of the rare gas at the end of the row in which the metal appears in the periodic chart. In counting the electrons, the appropriate oxidation state of the metal is assigned and each carbon monoxide that is present is presumed to bring in with it two electrons — the lone pair electrons in the orbital on carbon pointing away from oxygen. Thus in $Ni(CO)_4$, Ni in the zero oxidation state has 28 electrons; eight additional brought in by the four CO's gives 36, the electronic configuration of krypton. The bookkeeping procedure for $Mn_2(CO)_{10}$ would consist of considering $Mn° = 25$; $5 \times 2 = 10$ for the CO's; and each Mn contributing one electron to the other in the covalent Mn:Mn bond so that the total is 36 around each Mn. In $Fe_2(CO)_9$ (see the structure above) we can do the following accounting: $Fe° = 26$; three terminal CO's $= 6$; three bridging CO's each contribute one electron to each Fe; and finally the covalent Fe: Fe bond adds one additional electron to each Fe: $26 + 6 + 3 + 1 = 36$. The bridging CO's resemble the carbonyl group of a ketone $\frac{R}{R}{>}C{=}O$, while the terminal CO's resemble somewhat the uncomplexed carbon monoxide.

In resonance theory, the structure of carbon monoxide must be expressed as a resonance hybrid. The most important contribution comes from the valence bond structure $:C{\equiv}\overset{+}{O}:$ with a triple bond between the carbon and oxygen. The next most important structure is :C=Ö:. This structure implies a vacant p orbital on carbon. In this formulation the vacant orbital is an acceptor site and in this sense is equivalent to the π^* orbital in :C≡O. It is generally more satisfactory to regard carbon monoxide as essentially triply bonded with low-lying antibonding acceptor orbitals.

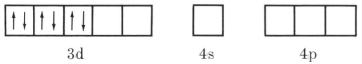

3d   4s   4p

FIGURE 3.3 • An Excited Electron Configuration of Cr°.

3.4 THE STRUCTURE OF THE METAL CARBONYLS

As we mentioned earlier in considering the electron distribution in CO, there is a lone pair of electrons on carbon in a predominantly p orbital pointing away from the oxygen. This orbital can overlap with a metal orbital to form a sigma bond. Let us consider the case of a typical carbonyl such as $Cr(CO)_6$. The ground state of neutral chromium, Cr°, has the configuration sd^5, but for our purposes it is more convenient to start with the excited configuration of Cr°, d^6, the electronic configuration of which may be indicated as shown in Fig. 3.3: Cr° uses six d^2sp^3 hybrid orbitals to form sigma bonds with the six carbons of the carbon monoxides that are arranged in an octahedron around the Cr. The six carbons each contributing their two electrons thus gives Cr an EAN of 36. Now all metals are characterized by being electropositive; metals prefer to lose electrons rather than gain them. The donation of six electrons into Cr would place substantial negative charge on the Cr. This charge on the Cr can be relieved by donation of electrons on the Cr back into orbitals on the carbon monoxide.* We have already seen that CO has π_x^* and π_y^* empty orbitals. These antibonding orbitals are mostly on the carbon. Most important, however, is the fact that the filled d orbitals on the Cr, d_{xy}, d_{xz}, d_{yz}, have the same arrangement (symmetry) of lobes as do the π^* orbitals and hence the interaction is very probable. The

---

* The tendency for the central metal atom in a complex to achieve zero electrical charge is generalized in the Principle of Electrical Neutrality, L. Pauling, *J. Chem. Soc.*, 1641 (1948).

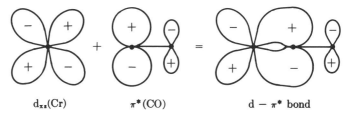

$d_{xz}(Cr)$ $\pi^*(CO)$ $d - \pi^*$ bond

FIGURE 3.4 • The Formation of a d→π^* Bond in Chromium Carbonyl.

interaction of one d orbital, say, the d_{xz}, with a π_x^* orbital on CO is illustrated in Fig. 3.4. This type of bonding, in which the filled d's on the metal overlap the π^* on the ligand, is frequently called back-bonding in order to emphasize the distinction from the sigma bonding or forward bonding in which the ligand furnishes the electrons. This back-bonding is of the d—π type (π and π^* both give the d—π type bond), and is often called dπ—pπ interaction.

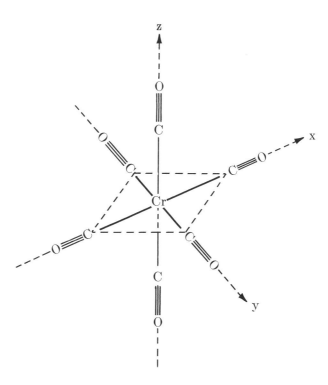

FIGURE 3.5 • The Octahedral Structure of Cr(CO)$_6$.

Hexacoordinated $Cr(CO)_6$ is an octahedral compound (Fig. 3.5) in which the ligands may be considered to lie along the x, y, and z axes. There are two ligands on each axis, one at each end. Let us examine the situation along, say, the x axis. The d_{xz} orbital on the metal is in the xz plane and the four lobes of the orbital are all half way between the x and z axes. Since there is only one such orbital, the π^* on both carbon monoxides at each end will be competing for the d_{xz} electrons (Fig. 3.6). Actually the CO's along the z axis also have π^*'s that compete for d_{xz} overlap so that four CO's compete for the d_{xz} — two on the x axis and two on the z axis. Four CO's also compete for the d_{yz} orbital, the two on the y axis and again the two on the z axis. The fact that the CO orbitals on the left end of the x axis, as in Fig. 3.6, are interchanged with respect to signs should

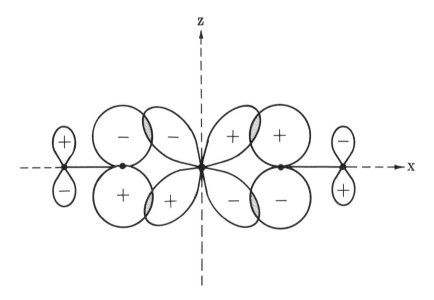

FIGURE 3.6 • The Interaction of a d Metal Orbital with Two Antibonding π^* Orbitals of CO.

not bother us; the bonding occurs because of the matching of signs, and we can place a minus or a plus sign at any lobe we start with just as long as we alternate signs on different sides of a node. In other words, we can always multiply a wavefunction by -1, which means we choose the minus sign on the square root of the normalization factor, which we arbitrarily ignored (cf. page 18). The fact that four CO's are competing for one d_{xz} orbital means that the back-bonding is divided between the four CO's. The d_{xy} orbital in the xy plane must be shared with all four CO's in the xy plane; the π_y^* on each CO has appropriate symmetry for accepting electrons from the d_{xy} (see Fig. 3.7).

Let us now consider the effect that partial occupation of the π_x^* and π_y^* of the CO has on the bonding between C and O. Before complexing with the Cr, the C and O were bonded by

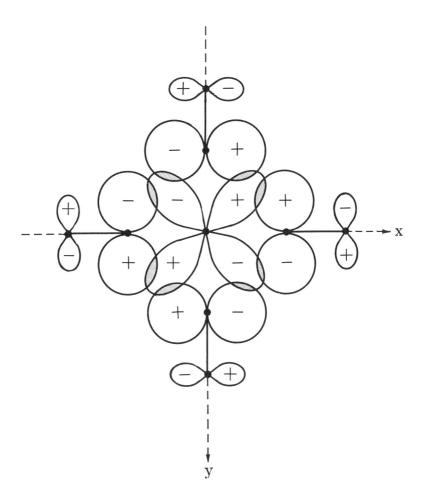

FIGURE 3.7 • The Interaction of a d Metal Orbital with Four Antibonding π^* Orbitals of CO.

the σ bond between them and by the two π bonds, π_x and π_y. We have seen that when electrons occupy antibonding orbitals, they cancel the bonding effect of electrons in bonding orbitals. This is precisely what happens in our metal carbonyl. The back donation of d electrons from the metal into antibonding orbitals of the CO reduces the π bonding between the C and O and there is no longer a net triple bond between these atoms as there is in the uncomplexed CO. The bond order of the carbon to oxygen bond has been reduced from about three in the free CO to something between two and three in the complexed CO.

We have discussed in considerable detail the structure of an octahedral complex. There are some differences in the structure of carbonyls with different geometries because different d orbitals are involved in both forward and back-bonding. Thus $Ni(CO)_4$ is a tetrahedral molecule and the d_{z^2} and $d_{x^2-y^2}$ orbitals of Ni are now involved in π rather than σ bonding, as in the octahedral case. In the trigonal bipyramidal geometry, say, of $Fe(CO)_5$ (Fig. 3.8), in which the metal atom uses dsp^3 hybrid orbitals, only one d orbital is involved in σ bonding and the other four d orbitals contribute to π bonding. However, the principles of σ and π bonding are essentially the same despite these differences.

The change in bond order of the C—O bond will, of course, affect the total strength of the C—O bonding; the higher the

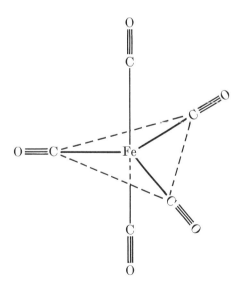

FIGURE 3.8 • The Trigonal Bipyramidal Structure of $Fe(CO)_5$.

bond order, the stronger the bond and the more energy one would have to apply in order to stretch or break the bond. There is an effective tool for measuring the energy required to stretch a bond. This measurement can be done by obtaining the infrared spectrum of the molecule because there is a characteristic stretching frequency for the C—O bond which varies with the bond order or resistance to stretch of the bond.

3.5 THE INFRARED SPECTRA OF SOME CARBONYLS

Molecules in the gas and liquid phase are in constant motion relative to each other. There is also, of course, considerable motion within the molecule. The atoms of the molecule move with respect to each other, and these motions may conveniently be described in terms of either the stretching or bending of bonds; i.e., the distance and angles between atoms are constantly changing, although there is always a preferred equilibrium position.

Modern quantum theory again teaches that vibrational energy can be accepted by the molecule only in discrete quanta, i.e., molecules exist in discrete vibrational states of well-defined energies. The spacing of these states, however, is much closer than the spacing of the electronic states discussed in the preceding chapter. Transitions to higher states can again be caused by absorption of appropriate energy from "light," only now the frequencies lie in the infrared region of the spectrum, about 300 to 3500 cm^{-1}, corresponding to energies of about 1–10 kcal/mole.

The energy required to stretch a bond between two atoms is related to the weight or mass of the two atoms and also to the stiffness of the bond. We would expect that the heavier the atoms and the more multiple-bonded they are, the more energy will be required to stretch the bond. In this respect, the bond may be considered as a spring — the stiffer the spring, the more difficult it is to stretch. If a ball is attached to a spring which is fixed to a wall at the other end, and if one pulls on the ball and stretches the spring, there is a considerable restoring force acting on the ball, which tends to bring it back to its equilibrium position. The restoring force (f) is proportional to the displacement, x: $f = (-k)x$. The constant k is called the force constant and its units are force per unit displacement, usually dynes/cm. If we were now to release the stretched spring, the ball would undergo vibratory motion. The frequency of the vibration is related to the force constant and the mass of the ball as follows:

$$\nu = \frac{1}{2\pi} \sqrt{k/m}.$$

The vibration of two atoms bonded to one another, stretched and released, can be described in the same way:

$$\nu = \frac{1}{2\pi} \sqrt{k/\mu} \tag{1}$$

where now μ is the so-called reduced mass: $\mu = \dfrac{m_1 m_2}{m_1 + m_2}$, where m_1 and m_2 are the masses of the bonded atoms. In a way, therefore, the reduced mass is the average mass of the two atoms. The force constant equation given above describes an harmonic oscillator, for which the equation of motion is the form of a parabola $y = kx^2/2$. One would therefore expect that the potential energy curve for a diatomic molecule would be a parabola. In fact, the curve is not a perfect parabola, but is the Morse curve introduced earlier, and shown in Fig. 3.9. However, for the lower vibrations the curve is excellently

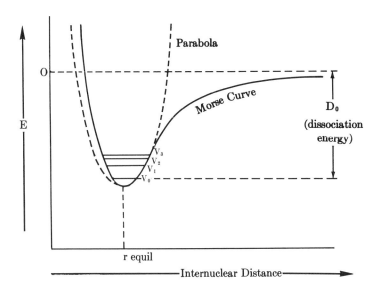

FIGURE 3.9 • The Morse Curve and the Potential Energy Curve for the Harmonic Oscillator.

approximated by the parabola. The horizontal lines represent vibrational quantum levels. If the molecule behaved like a perfect harmonic oscillator, the distance between vibrational levels would be constant; in real cases the distances become less at higher vibrational levels, resulting in a compression of levels. In the normal or ground state of molecules, each molecule is in the lowest or zero vibrational level (v_0) and when exposed to infrared radiation of the appropriate wavelength or frequency (energy), the molecule gets promoted to a higher vibrational level, usually v_1.

According to Eq. (1), if we kept the reduced mass, μ, the same or nearly the same in a series of compounds, the frequency should be proportional to $\sqrt{k}$. The series of hydrogen halides illustrates this point. The reduced masses, in atomic mass units, for the series are

$$\mu_{HF} = \frac{1 \times 19}{20} = .95; \quad \mu_{HCl} = \frac{1 \times 35}{36} = .97;$$

$$\mu_{HBr} = \frac{1 \times 80}{81} = .99; \quad \mu_{HI} = \frac{1 \times 127}{128} = .99$$

and the frequencies and force constants are shown in Table 1.

TABLE 1   **Spectra of Hydrogen Halides[a]**

Halide	$k(10^5$ dynes/cm)	$\sqrt{k}$	$\nu(cm^{-1})$
HF	8.8	2.97	3958
HCl	4.8	2.19	2885
HBr	3.8	1.95	2559
HI	2.9	1.70	2230

[a] R. S. Drago, "Physical Methods in Inorganic Chemistry" (New York, Reinhold Publishing Corp., 1965), p. 190.

With this little background we shall take a very restricted look at the infrared spectra of some carbonyl complexes.* A

---

* It must be appreciated that infrared spectroscopy is a very complicated and complex subject. The geometry of the complex, i.e., whether it is tetrahedral, octahedral, etc., affects the number and type of vibrations which may occur, but we shall not go into these symmetry considerations. Furthermore, the operation of the so-called selection rules determines the intensities of particular absorption bands. Despite our very abbreviated exposure, it is possible to focus in a meaningful way on the $C-O$ bonding and show how the infrared stretching frequency is affected by the extent of interaction of the metal d orbitals with the antibonding orbitals of CO.

variety of factors affect the frequency of CO infrared absorption. First, we would expect to have a different energy of absorption depending on whether the CO is uncomplexed, or is complexed as a bridging or a terminal CO. Free carbon monoxide has an absorption band at $\nu = 2150$ cm^{-1}. A terminal CO usually absorbs around 2000 cm^{-1}. In free CO, the CO is approximately a triple bond. In the terminal complexed CO, as we have seen, there is back-donation from filled metal d's into π^*'s of CO and hence partial cancellation of C to O bonding. The reduction in bond order on complexing reduces the force constant and hence the bond can be stretched with less energy. The back-bonding is the principal explanation for the fact that the terminal CO has a stretching frequency of about 150 cm^{-1} less than un-complexed CO. A bridging C=O resembles a CO in an organic carbonyl compound like a ketone which absorbs at about 1700 cm^{-1}. In such a carbonyl group there is no back-bonding (the π^* orbital is too high in energy) and the C to O bond is pretty much a double bond. Bridging CO's usually show two stretch-ing frequencies: 1850 and 1700 cm^{-1}, considerably lower than the terminally complexed CO, and close to the ketone region. The relationship between force constant, bond length, and stretching frequency for various kinds of carbonyl groups is shown in Table 2.

TABLE 2   **Force Constants, Bond Lengths and Stretching Frequencies of Various Carbonyl Groups**

Compound	ν_{C-O}(cm^{-1})	k(10^5 dynes/cm)[a]	C—O length (A)[a]
C=O	2150	18.6	1.13
Ni(C=O)$_4$	2057	16.2	1.15
CH$_2$=C=O	1935	14.5	1.17
H$_2$C=O	1750	12.1	1.21

[a] From Wender, Sternberg, and Orchin, "The Oxo Reaction," in P. H. Emmett, ed., *Catalysis*, Vol. V (New York: Reinhold Publishing Corp., 1957), p. 92.

A second factor affecting the stretching frequency of a com-plexed CO is the oxidation state of the metal atom to which the CO is complexed. Because back-donation from the metal into antibonding π^*'s on the CO's is a function of the availability of the metal d orbitals, other things being equal, we would expect that the greater the positive charge or oxidation number, the more reluctant the metal would be to permit its d electrons to participate in back-bonding. The less the back-bonding, the less cancellation of C to O bonding and the more the C to O bond is triple bond in character. The more triple bond, the larger the force constant and therefore the higher the stretching frequency. Table 3 gives data on the spectra of a series of cyclo-

TABLE 3   Carbonyl Stretching Frequencies of Some Carbonyls of the Structure $[C_5H_5M(CO)_3]^n$ (n = formal oxidation no.)[a]

Metal	n	$\nu_{C-O}(cm^{-1})$
Fe	+1	2120, 2070
Mn	0	2035, 1953
Cr	−1	1876, 1695
V	−2	1748, 1645

[a] A. Davison, M. L. H. Green, and G. Wilkinson, *J. Chem. Soc.*, 3172 (1961).

pentadienyl metal tricarbonyl complexes in which the oxidation state of the first row transition metal series is varied. These complexes all involve a cyclopentadienyl group π bonded to the transition metal along with three CO molecules. The geometry of the complex resembles a piano stool with the cyclopentadienyl group ⬠ as the seat and the three CO's as the legs of the stool, both seat and legs being centrally fastened to the metal. The data are nicely explained by the increasing occupation of the antibonding orbitals of the CO's.

Essentially the same kind of reasoning explains the data of Table 4. Here are four series of compounds. In each series the same number of CO's are attached to the central metal atom (so as to distribute the amount of charge transfer equally), but the formal oxidation number n of the central metal atom is

TABLE 4   Carbonyl Stretching Frequencies in Some Carbonyls and Carbonyl Anions[a]

Compound	n[b]	$\nu_{C-O}(cm^{-1})$	Compound	n	$\nu_{C-O}(cm^{-1})$
$Ni(CO)_4$	0	2057	$Fe(CO)_5$	0	2034, 2014
$[Co(CO)_4]^-$	−1	1886	$[Mn(CO)_5]^-$	−1	1898, 1863
$[Fe(CO)_4]^{--}$	−2	1786			
$Mn_2(CO)_{10}$	0	2074, 2015, 1972	$Re_2(CO)_{10}$	0	2049, 2013, 1983
$[Cr_2(CO)_{10}]^{--}$	−1	1945, 1922, 1897	$[W_2(CO)_{10}]^{--}$	−1	1944, 1906, 1882

[a] W. Hieber, G. Braun, and W. Beck, *Chem. Ber.* **93**, 901 (1960).
[b] Formal oxidation number.

varied. It will be noted that the four-coordinated (tetrahedral) complexes have one stretching frequency, the five-coordinated (trigonal bipyramid) have two, and the six-coordinated [$M_2(CO)_{10}$ compounds are two octahedra joined at a corner] have three stretching frequencies. The number of infrared active stretching frequencies depends greatly upon the geometry (symmetry) of the complex in a manner which is beyond the scope of this book to explore. The important point to be made from the data of Table 4 is that, as negative charge is built up on the metal, the metal has an increasing desire to share its d electrons with the CO which has empty antibonding π^* orbitals. Hence C to O bonding is diminished, the C—O force constant reduced, and the frequency lowered.

4

Ultraviolet Absorption Spectroscopy and Photochemistry

4.1 SOME FUNDAMENTAL PRINCIPLES

In the last chapter we discussed vibrations of molecules, in particular the stretching vibrations of free CO and CO complexed to various transition metals. These vibrations required relatively little energy, and such energy can be furnished by radiation in the infrared region; absorption of such energy by the molecule results in changes in the vibrational energy levels of the molecule. Electronic changes, i.e., the promotion of an electron from one molecular electronic level to a higher level, require very much more energy than vibrational changes. Electronic transitions may occur when molecules capable of undergoing such transitions are exposed to light in the ultraviolet and visible region of the electromagnetic spectrum. For most experimental purposes, this region is in the frequency range of 50,000 cm^{-1} to about 13,000 cm^{-1} (200 mμ to 780 mμ equivalent to about $143 - 38$ kcal./mole).

Electronic spectra of atoms are line spectra, since in atoms there are generally relatively few, widely separated electronic states. In molecules, there are also few electronic states, but each has associated with it a long series of more closely spaced vibrational substates and each of these, in turn, has a series of very closely spaced rotational levels (cf. Fig. 4.1). Consequently, any single electronic transition in a molecule consists of a multitude of lines, which can only be separated by the most elaborate techniques with extremely sensitive instruments. Thus, in normal spectrometers, the absorptions appear as bands and are called band spectra. In addition, in the liquid phase,

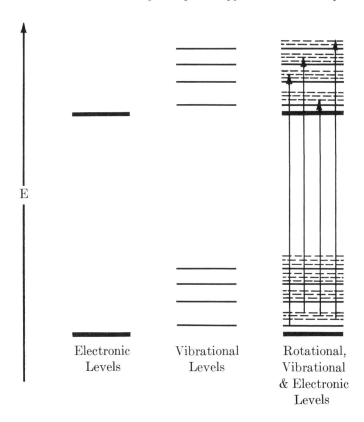

Electronic
Levels

Vibrational
Levels

Rotational,
Vibrational
& Electronic
Levels

FIGURE 4.1 • An Electronic Transition Giving Rise to a Band Structure.

in which most observations are made, rotational and vibrational structure is broadened compared with vapor spectra, leading to the usually observed broad, smooth bands.

Ultraviolet spectra are usually plotted in a coordinate system in which the abscissa is a measure of the energy (wavelength, λ, or frequency, ν) and the ordinate is a measure of the intensity of the absorption bands.

The energy of a transition is directly related to the frequency in accordance with the Bohr condition: $\Delta E = E_u - E_l = h\nu$ where E_u is the energy of the upper state and the E_l the energy of the lower state. The energy required for the longest wavelength (smallest frequency, smallest energy) electronic transition in a molecule is related to the energy difference between the highest occupied and the lowest unoccupied molecular orbitals; the latter one is usually an antibonding one. Knowledge of the molecular orbitals and their energies is thus obviously a great aid in understanding and predicting electronic spectra. On the other hand, having determined the spectrum of a compound, it is of obvious value to attempt to identify an observed absorption band with a particular transition.

The intensity of a particular absorption band (the ordinate in the usual representation of spectra) depends on the probability that the transition will occur. This probability in turn depends on what are called selection rules — rules that derive from symmetry considerations, from considerations relating to the spin of the electrons involved, and other factors; the discussion of all these is beyond the scope of this book. The intensity usually is reported as either absorbance, A, or molar extinction coefficient, ϵ. The relationship between these is given by $A = \epsilon c$ where c is the concentration of the compound in moles per liter. The absorbance is equal to the ratio of the log of the intensity of the incident light to the intensity of the transmitted light: $A = \log I_0/I$. The absorbance is usually measured directly in the ultraviolet spectrophotometer.

Obviously we cannot hope to cover in a few paragraphs the essentials of the field of ultraviolet spectroscopy. We will, however, attempt to study a few systems to demonstrate again the importance of antibonding orbitals for an understanding of electronic spectral phenomena.

4.2 THE SIMPLE CARBONYL $\left(\!\!\begin{array}{c}\diagdown\\[-2pt]\diagup\end{array}\!\!C{=}O\right)$ CHROMOPHORE

Molecules, or characteristic groups of atoms, which have π orbitals absorb ultraviolet or visible radiation, and particular groupings give rise to characteristic absorption bands. These groups of atoms, usually containing π orbitals, are called chromophores. Examples are the carbonyl group $\left(\!\!\begin{array}{c}\diagdown\\[-2pt]\diagup\end{array}\!\!C{=}O\right)$, the nitro group $\left(-N\diagup^{O}_{\diagdown O}\right)$, and the benzene nucleus $\left(\!\!\boxed{\bigcirc}\!\!\right)$.

First we shall examine the electronic structure of an organic molecule with a simple carbonyl chromophore — formaldehyde.

Formaldehyde has a σ bond skeleton in which the carbon atom is attached to two hydrogen atoms and an oxygen atom by single bonds (Fig. 4.2). The carbon atom bonded to two hydro-

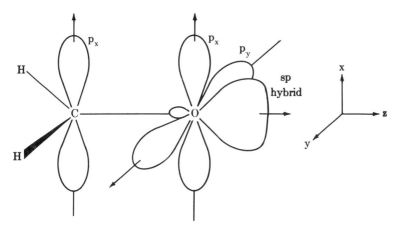

FIGURE 4.2 • The Orbitals of Formaldehyde.

gen atoms and an oxygen atom uses sp^2 hybrid orbitals directed at angles of about 120° from each other to form the sigma skeleton. This leaves a p orbital with one electron in it, the p_x orbital. The oxygen atom uses an sp hybrid orbital to bond to carbon and the second sp orbital points away from the carbon atom. This latter orbital accommodates a lone pair of electrons. Bookkeeping will be facilitated by reference to Fig. 4.3. One electron remains in a p_x orbital which can combine with the electron in a similar orbital on carbon to generate a π bonding and a π^* antibonding orbital. The two electrons originating from p_x atomic orbitals occupy the π bonding orbital with a node in the yz plane, the molecular plane shown in Fig. 4.2. Finally the other p orbital on oxygen, p_y, in the yz plane accommodates the other lone pair electrons on oxygen, which are commonly called n electrons.

The promotion of electrons out of σ bonding orbitals requires a great deal of energy because the bond must be broken in the

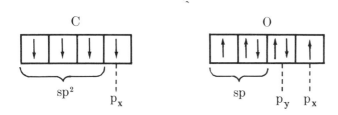

FIGURE 4.3 • The Electronic Configuration of Carbon and Oxygen in Formaldehyde.

process and, if it did occur, would very likely lead to disruption (dissociation) of the molecule. The electrons of interest in understanding the spectrum of formaldehyde are the electrons in the π bonding orbital and the n electrons in the p_y orbital on the oxygen atom. The other lone pair electrons on the oxygen are in an sp orbital and, because of the s character, much more tightly held by the oxygen than the lone pair in the p_y orbital.

The orbitals of interest can be related in terms of the molecular orbital level diagram (Fig. 4.4). In this abbreviated diagram we are neglecting the sigma skeleton and concentrating on the lone pairs on oxygen and the combination of pπ's on the carbon and oxygen.

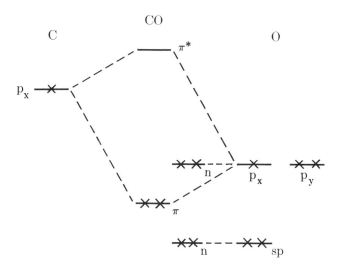

FIGURE 4.4 • The Molecular Orbital Energy Diagram for the Carbonyl Group.

4.3 THE n → π* TRANSITION

Fig. 4.4 shows that in the carbonyl system, the electronic transition requiring the least energy is the promotion of an electron from the n level on the oxygen atom to the antibonding π* level. Up to this point we have discussed bonding and anti-bonding orbitals. We must now introduce a third type of molecular orbital — the *non-bonding* orbital. As the name suggests, this is a type of orbital which makes no contribution to the binding energy of the molecule, or better, electrons occupying such an orbital make no such contribution. Non-bonding orbitals are of two types:

(1) An orbital which accommodates lone-pair electrons and which is a pure atomic orbital, or a hybrid atomic orbital of one atom only. That a lone pair of electrons make no contribution to the binding energy seems obvious since they are not shared by any pair of atoms.

(2) True delocalized molecular orbitals are non-bonding if no contributions are made by atomic orbitals from any pair of adjacent atoms. Consider, for example, the π molecular orbitals of CO_2, shown in Fig. 4.5. ψ_2 is non-bonding since it receives no contribution from carbon pπ orbitals, and because the oxygen pπ orbitals are too far apart to overlap significantly.

In what follows, we shall only consider the lone pair orbitals discussed under (1) above, which will be denoted n orbitals (n for *n*on-bonding).

The lowest energy transition involved, Fig. 4.4, is called an n to π^* transition and is indicated as n $\rightarrow$ π^*. In formaldehyde this transition gives rise to an absorption band at about 270 mμ. This band is a relatively weak band ($\epsilon = \sim100$) which means that the transition, in the first approximation, is a forbidden transition (forbidden does not mean that it never occurs but that it is highly improbable). We say that this is a symmetry forbidden transition. The reasons for the forbiddenness can be crudely justified by the fact that the π^* orbital, like the π orbital, is in the xz plane (Fig. 4.2), while the p_y orbital having the n electrons is in the yz plane and hence perpendicular to the π^* orbital. Since the regions in space of the two orbitals overlap so poorly, the likelihood of the transition from one to the other is quite low. The fact that it occurs at all is probably due to the vibrations of the atoms which include some twisting which in turn increases overlap. Thus, although the symmetry selection rule predicts zero intensity, vibrational interaction makes the transition partially allowed.

Further evidence for the correct identification of the 270 mμ band in formaldehyde as an n $\rightarrow$ π^* transition comes from a study of solvent effects. When the spectrum of this and other carbonyl compounds is determined in ethanol, the absorption band appears at shorter wavelength than when the spectrum

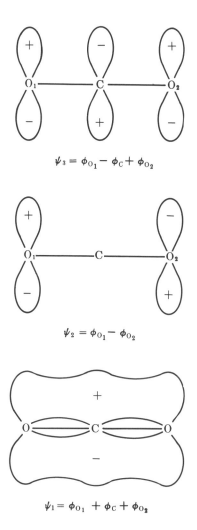

$$\psi_3 = \phi_{O_1} - \phi_C + \phi_{O_2}$$

$$\psi_2 = \phi_{O_1} - \phi_{O_2}$$

$$\psi_1 = \phi_{O_1} + \phi_C + \phi_{O_2}$$

FIGURE 4.5 • Three of the Molecular Orbitals of CO_2.

is determined in a hydrocarbon solvent such as hexane. A shift to shorter wavelength (higher frequency, higher energy) is called a hypsochromic or blue shift, while a shift in the opposite direction (to longer wavelength, lower frequency, or lower energy) is called a red or bathochromic shift. In a hydroxylic solvent we would expect the carbonyl group to be hydrogen-bonded to the solvent through the lone pair (p_y) electrons on oxygen:

$$\diagdown \text{C} \!=\! \text{O} : \cdots \text{H} \!-\! \text{O}$$
$$|$$
$$\text{R}$$

Since the $n \rightarrow \pi^*$ transition involves the promotion of an n electron, it would be necessary to break the hydrogen bond in the promotion process. This would require more energy than would be the case were the carbonyl group not hydrogen-bonded as in the hydrocarbon solvent. Since the fundamental absorption equation is $E = h\nu = hc/\lambda$, if the energy is increased, the frequency at which absorption occurs is also increased, thus accounting for the observed blue shift. This blue shift can actually be used to obtain a crude measure of the hydrogen bond strength.

4.4 SINGLET AND TRIPLET STATES

In the ground (or normal) state of molecules, the pair of electrons in each molecular orbital are necessarily paired, i.e., they have opposed or antiparallel spin. This fact arises from the operation of the Pauli exclusion principle (no two electrons can have all four quantum numbers identical); if two electrons are in the same orbital, three of their quantum numbers are identical and so their fourth quantum number, the spin quantum number, must be different. Spin quantum numbers have the values of either $\pm \frac{1}{2}$. The total spin quantum number of a molecule is called J, and the multiplicity of the state is given by $J = |2S| + 1$, where $S =$ the sum of the spins of the individual

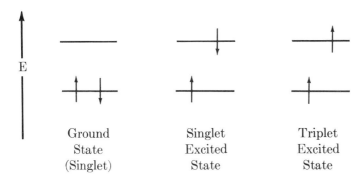

FIGURE 4.6 • Singlet and Triplet States.

electrons. When the two electrons are (necessarily) paired in an orbital, $S = +\frac{1}{2} - \frac{1}{2} = 0$ and $J = 1$. In this situation, the molecule is said to be in the singlet state. When the molecule is excited and an electron is promoted from an orbital in which it is paired to another and empty orbital, the pairing restriction is removed because now the electrons are in different orbitals. Now the electrons can be either (a) paired, in which case the excited molecule is in the singlet state, or (b) the electrons can have parallel spins in which case the multiplicity is 3 since $S = +\frac{1}{2} + \frac{1}{2} = 1$ or $-\frac{1}{2} - \frac{1}{2} = -1$ and $J = |2S| + 1 = 3$. (The vertical bars mean absolute value without regard to algebraic sign.) When the spins are unpaired or parallel, the molecule is said to be in the triplet (see Fig. 4.6) state.*

In the previous section we considered one of the selection rules, namely the symmetry forbidden character of the $n \rightarrow \pi^*$ transition. Another selection rule states that changes in multiplicity, e.g., a singlet to triplet transition, during an excitation are forbidden, to the point that they may be observed only under specially favorable conditions. Virtually all stable molecules (except compounds of transition metals and rare earths) have singlet ground states.

Let us now return to our carbonyl compound which has a singlet ground state (Fig. 4.4) which we will denote by S_0. The $n \rightarrow \pi^*$ excitation leads to two excited states — a singlet excited state S_1, and a triplet excited state T_1 — and thus absorption at two different frequencies might be expected. The absorption we observe must be $S_1 \leftarrow S_0$ (read S_1 from S_0), because the transition $T_1 \leftarrow S_0$ is too highly forbidden to be observable. Similarly, nearly all absorption bands observed in ordinary absorption spectroscopy of organic compounds correspond to singlet-singlet transitions.

Once a molecule undergoes a singlet-singlet transition to the first excited singlet state, S_1, the excited molecule can lose its energy by several processes which will be elaborated below. One way it may lose its excitation energy is to cross over from the singlet state S_1 to the lower energy T_1 state by loss of vibrational energy (see Fig. 4.7). Although this so-called intersystem

---

* This state is called a triplet because, in the presence of a magnetic field, the state splits into three energy levels depending on the three possible different orientations of the spins of the individual electrons. A singlet state, on the other hand, is not split by a magnetic field because there is only one possible orientation of the electrons; hence the name singlet.

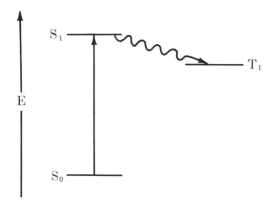

FIGURE 4.7 • Electronic Transition to the Singlet State and Non-radiative Crossover to the Triplet State.

crossing is formally forbidden because of the change in multiplicity, it can occur with high efficiency in certain kinds of molecules, especially aromatic and carbonyl-containing compounds. The triplet state is always lower in energy than the corresponding singlet state. The energy relationship may be rationalized by pointing out that two electrons will not get very close together in space if their spins are parallel, i.e., they cannot get close enough to share each other's orbital even partly since, in doing so, they would be violating the Pauli exclusion principle. Because the unpaired electrons are thus farther apart in space, electron-electron repulsion is minimized and the energy of the triplet state is lower than that of the corresponding excited singlet.

4.5 $\pi \rightarrow \pi^*$ TRANSITIONS

If we return to Fig. 4.4 we see that not only should we expect the $n \rightarrow \pi^*$ transition, but that we should also expect a $\pi \rightarrow \pi^*$ transition in formaldehyde. We also see from the figure that this latter transition should occur at shorter wavelength (higher frequency) than the $n \rightarrow \pi^*$ transition. In formaldehyde, the $\pi \rightarrow \pi^*$ transition cannot be observed on most ultraviolet spectrophotometers. However, with appropriate equipment (a vacuum spectrometer), the transition is observed at about 185 mμ.

In Fig. 4.2 we showed the π orbital in the xz plane. Although the π^* orbital is not shown, it is also in the xz plane. This means that when sufficient energy is imparted to the molecule to effect the $\pi \rightarrow \pi^*$ promotion, the transition occurs with a high probability. Accordingly, the $\pi \rightarrow \pi^*$ transition gives rise to a high intensity absorption band ($\epsilon \simeq 10^4$ to 10^5).

All conjugated dienes and all aromatic systems have delocalized π systems, but no n electrons. The molecular orbitals of spectroscopic interest are π and π^* orbitals and therefore all transitions in these systems are of the $\pi \rightarrow \pi^*$ variety.

We saw that solvents have a great influence on the $n \rightarrow \pi^*$ transition; hydrogen-bonding solvents give blue shifts. In considering the effects of solvents on the $\pi \rightarrow \pi^*$ transition we ask ourselves how the polarity of a solvent separately affects the ground and excited states. In general we know that the excited state is more polar than the ground state. We need only recall that the ground state of butadiene, for example, is best represented by the structure $CH_2{=}CH{-}CH{=}CH_2$. The excited state must be represented by a group of structures nearly all of which involve charge-separated species, e.g.:

$$^+CH_2{-}CH{=}CH{-}CH_2{}^- \leftrightarrow {}^-CH_2{-}CH{=}CH{-}CH_2{}^+$$

$$\leftrightarrow {}^+CH_2{-}{}^-CH{-}CH{=}CH_2, \text{ etc.}$$

A polar solvent may be expected to stabilize the excited state more than the ground state and hence the energy separating the two states is reduced. Therefore, polar solvents produce bathochromic shifts of the $\pi \rightarrow \pi^*$ transition, whereas, as we have seen, such solvents produce hypsochromic shifts of the $n \rightarrow \pi^*$ transitions.

4.6 THE RELATIVE ENERGIES OF EXCITED STATES

Just as the $n \rightarrow \pi^*$ excited state can exist in either a singlet or triplet state, so the $\pi \rightarrow \pi^*$ excited state can exist as either a singlet or triplet. The $n \rightarrow \pi^*$ excited singlet is definitely lower in energy than the $\pi \rightarrow \pi^*$ singlet and we know that the triplet of each state is lower than the singlet of the corresponding state. If we assume that the difference in energy between the singlet and triplet in each excited state is the same, we would have an energy diagram resembling Fig. 4.8a. However, the singlet-triplet separation is known to be very much less for the $n \rightarrow \pi^*$ excited state than it is for the $\pi \rightarrow \pi^*$ state. There are some situations in which the energy differences are such that

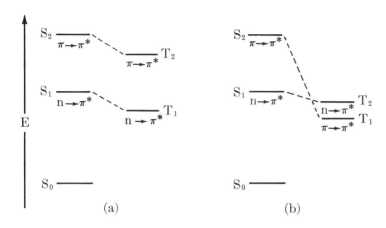

FIGURE 4.8 • Singlet-Triplet Energy Levels. (a) Usual Arrangement with $n \rightarrow \pi^*$ Lowest; (b) Lowest Level as $\pi \rightarrow \pi^*$.

the lowest triplet is the $\pi \rightarrow \pi^*$ triplet rather than the $n \rightarrow \pi^*$ (Fig. 4.8b). The chemical significance of these energy relationships are profound and will be touched on later.

4.7 THE FATE OF EXCITED MOLECULES

The absorption of light by a molecule raises the molecule to a higher electronic state. Let us now briefly summarize the ways in which the excited molecule can lose its energy (Fig. 4.9). In this figure, solid lines represent radiative processes (a is absorption and b and f are emission) while the wavy lines represent non-radiative processes where the energy is lost by collision or by vibrational changes, all of which release heat and hence are called thermal decay processes. After the molecule is excited, say to its S_1 state, it can undergo one of four energy-degrading steps; three of these are shown in Fig. 4.9. The molecule may emit a quantum of light (b); this process is called fluorescence. Or it may lose its energy in the form of heat (c) by vibrational decay on collision (called internal conversion). Or it may undergo intersystem crossing to T_1(d) — a non-radiative process—from which state the molecule can either emit a quantum of light (f) in a process called phosphorescence, or the T_1 state can return to S_0 by thermal decay (e), also called internal conversion. The fourth possibility in tracing the fate of the excited molecule is the possibility of transferring its energy to another molecule; if this occurs, the excited or donor molecule returns to its ground state and the acceptor molecule gets excited. If the donor was in the triplet state at the time of its energy transfer, the acceptor molecule gets promoted to its triplet state — and similarly we would expect singlet-singlet energy transfer. However, because the triplet state exists for a much longer period of time (usually between 1 sec. and 10^{-3} sec.) than a singlet state (lifetimes of about 10^{-8} to 10^{-7} sec.), it has a greater possibility of transferring its energy to another molecule. Hence triplet-triplet transfer is much more common than singlet-singlet transfer. The longer lifetime of the triplet is understood when it is appreciated that, in order for the triplet to return to the ground state, it must undergo a spin inversion. Doing this by a radiative process (phosphorescence)* is formally forbidden; hence of low probability and thus the possibility of other modes of energy transfer occurring is increased. As we shall see, triplet-triplet energy transfer has many practical implications.

4.8 CHEMISTRY OF THE EXCITED STATE. PHOTOCHEMISTRY

4.81 MORSE CURVES OF EXCITED STATES

Let us for the moment return to the hydrogen molecule. We have seen that the total energy as a function of internuclear

---

* Phosphorescence was first identified correctly by G. N. Lewis and M. Kasha, *J. Am. Chem. Soc.*, **66**, 2100 (1944). These workers showed that each substance has a unique phosphorescent state and they calculated from the phosphorescence spectra the energy separation (triplet energy) between the phosphorescent state (T_1) and the ground state (S_0) of 89 compounds. Gilbert N. Lewis was born in Massachusetts in 1875. He received all of his formal education at Harvard University, and was awarded a Ph.D. in 1899. After six years of teaching at Harvard, he moved to the Massachusetts Institute of Technology where he taught until 1912. From 1912 to 1946 he was Professor of Chemistry at the University of California at Berkeley. He died of a heart attack, while working in his laboratory, on March 23, 1946. He is regarded as the Father of Physical Chemistry in the United States.

Professor Michael Kasha was born in Elizabeth, New Jersey, in 1920. He received his undergraduate training at the University of Michigan and did his graduate work with G. N. Lewis at California. After some postdoctoral experience, he became professor at Florida State University and since 1960 has been director of the Institute of Molecular Biophysics there.

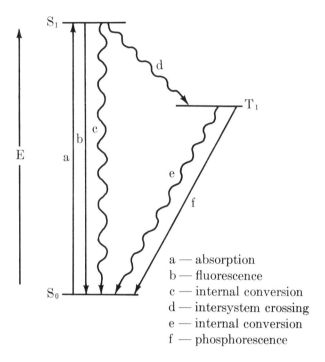

a — absorption
b — fluorescence
c — internal conversion
d — intersystem crossing
e — internal conversion
f — phosphorescence

FIGURE 4.9 • The Possible Routes to Loss of Excitation Energy.

distance for the ground state molecule may be expressed by a Morse curve (curve A in Fig. 4.10). We have also seen that promotion of one electron from the bonding to the antibonding molecular orbital slightly more than cancels the bonding contribution of the electron remaining in the bonding molecular orbital. The result of this situation is shown in Fig. 4.10 in the potential energy curve B, which is called a repulsive curve. What happens when we excite one electron from σ_g to σ_u^*? The molecule was vibrating, i.e., the two H atoms were moving periodically together and apart along the short horizontal line in curve A; in other words the bond distance was oscillating around its equilibrium value. Excitation now raises the molecule along the arrow to curve B, but the relative motion of the atoms persists. As soon as the atoms now move apart there is no potential to reverse the motion as in A and the atoms fly apart. This is called dissociation, or more explicitly *photo-*

dissociation, and it is the simplest photochemical process. It occurs not only in H_2, but may occur in any diatomic molecule which is held together by a single bond, and in many polyatomic molecules as well.

There is one restriction, however. If the excitation energy is lost before the atoms are very far apart by dropping to the excited vibrational level v_x, the molecule is "saved"; it fails to dissociate. The time scale here is quite interesting. The time required for a molecule to execute a vibration is of the order of 10^{-12} to 10^{-13} sec. Thus, the molecule is saved only if the energy loss follows the excitation within an extremely short time period.

For more complex molecules, there usually are additional states between the attractive and repulsive states of Fig. 4.10. Fig. 4.11 shows such a possibility where curve C now represents such an additional state. We can now observe two types of behavior. Excitation to a low vibrational level of curve C (arrow a) behaves like a normal electronic transition. But excitation to a high vibrational level of curve C (arrow b) places the molecule energetically above the intersection of curves B and C. Its vibrational motion on curve C from points x to y

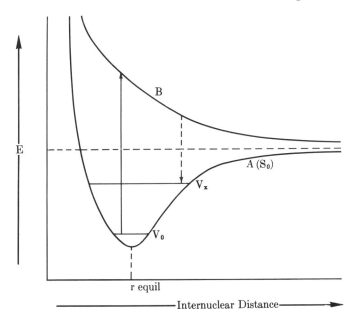

FIGURE 4.10 • The Morse Curves Showing Photodissociation.

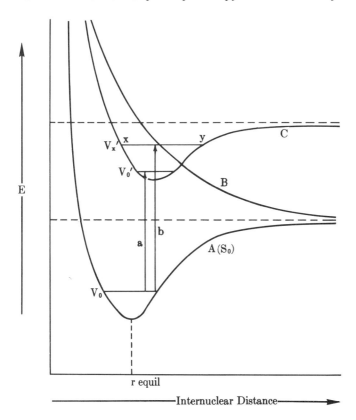

FIGURE 4.11 • The Morse Curves Showing Predissociation.

and back passes this intersection point, and there is a real chance that the molecule "loses its way" and continues on curve B, which again results in the molecules flying apart. This process is called *predissociation*, and is very common in heavy diatomic and polyatomic molecules.

4.82 THE CARBONYL GROUP

In the ground state, the carbonyl group is very strongly polarized toward the oxygen atom. This fact is expressed in the polarized resonance structure: $>C=O \leftrightarrow {}^+C—O^-$, and is consistent with the greater electronegativity of oxygen (3.5) as compared to carbon (2.5). Also the carbonyl group has a large dipole moment directed toward the oxygen. In the $n \rightarrow \pi^*$ excited state, an electron, formerly the exclusive property of oxygen, is now in an antibonding orbital which is principally on carbon (Fig. 4.4). Hence the antibonding orbital opposes the polarity which characterized the ground state, and the dipole moment of the carbonyl group in the excited state is very much reduced as compared to the ground state.

Many of the photochemical reactions of carbonyl groups indicate that the reactive $n \to \pi^*$ excited species is a triplet state. One of the oldest known reactions of carbonyl groups is their photoreduction to pinacols in the presence of hydrogen donors. Thus with benzophenone:

$$\begin{matrix} \Phi \\ \diagdown \\ \diagup \\ \Phi \end{matrix} C{=}O + RH \xrightarrow{h\nu} \quad \begin{matrix} & OH & \\ \Phi\diagdown & | & \diagup\Phi \\ & C{-}C & \\ \Phi\diagup & | \diagdown\Phi & \\ & OH & \end{matrix} \quad + R{-}R$$

Substantial work has shown rather conclusively that the benzophenone is in the triplet state when it abstracts hydrogen. The process involves, first, the irradiation of the mixture with appropriate light, whereupon the benzophenone undergoes $S_0 \to S_1(n \to \pi^*)$, followed by S_1 intersystem crossing to T_1. This triplet, with two unpaired electrons, behaves somewhat like a diradical $\Phi_2{-}\dot{C}{-}\dot{O}$, with one unshared electron each on C and O. This relatively long-lived species (it is a triplet) abstracts a hydrogen atom from the donor. The acceptor site on the diradical is oxygen rather than carbon because the singly occupied $p_y(n)$ orbital on oxygen is much more available than the singly occupied π^* orbital principally on carbon. The energetics are also more favorable since the O—H bond is more stable than the C—H bond. Finally, two $\Phi_2\dot{C}{-}OH$ radicals thus formed couple to give the pinacol, and two radicals R· from the donor couple to give R—R; and mixed dimers are formed from coupling of $\Phi_2\dot{C}{-}OH$ and R· :

$$\Phi_2 C{=}O + R{-}H \longrightarrow \begin{matrix} OH \\ | \\ \Phi_2 C{-}C\Phi_2 \\ | \\ OH \end{matrix} + \begin{matrix} OH \\ | \\ \Phi_2 C{-}R \end{matrix} + R{-}R$$

It is of interest to note that certain highly conjugated ketones

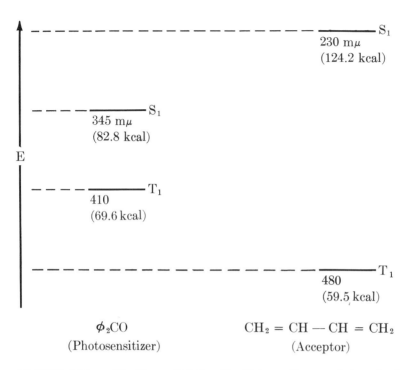

$\phi_2 CO$ $CH_2 = CH - CH = CH_2$
(Photosensitizer)   (Acceptor)

FIGURE 4.12 • The Energy Relationships Between Donor and Acceptor in a Photosensitized Reaction.

such as 1-acetylnaphthalene, ⬡⬡ , are very inert to photo-
                                                COCH₃
chemical reduction. It is now fairly certain that the reason for
this is that the lowest triplet is not the n → π* triplet (see Fig.
4.8a), but the π → π* triplet (see Fig. 4.8b). In the π → π*
triplet there is no free radical character on oxygen and hence
little tendency for hydrogen abstraction.

4.83   PHOTOSENSITIZERS

One of the most important processes in organic photochemistry
involves the transfer of electronic excitation from one molecule
to another. This may be written as follows, using benzophenone
as a donor (D) and butadiene as an acceptor (A):

(1) $D(S_0) \xrightarrow{h\nu} D(S_1)$

(2) $D(S_1) \longrightarrow D(T_1)$

(3) $D(T_1) + A(S_0) \longrightarrow D(S_0) + A(T_1)$

The energy relationships are shown in Fig. 4.12*. When benzophenone and butadiene are mixed and irradiated with light of about 350 mμ, the Φ_2CO absorbs the radiation and is excited to its S_1 state because of the n $\rightarrow \pi^*$ transition at 345 mμ which is the lowest energy transition of the molecule. Because of efficient intersystem crossing, the n $\rightarrow \pi^*$ triplet $D(T_1)$ is formed. This step (Eq. 2) is energetically favorable by 13.2 kcal/mole. The benzophenone n $\rightarrow \pi^*$ triplet then collides with ground state butadiene (Eq. 3) and promotes the latter to its triplet state, returning itself to its own ground state. The butadiene in its triplet state may now undergo a photochemical reaction. Thus absorption of light by benzophenone (the photosensitizer) effects ultimately the photochemical transformation of butadiene which would have been inert to radiation at 350 mμ, since its absorption above 250 mμ is negligible. In order to be a good photosensitizer, the molecule should have singlet and triplet states between the singlet and triplet states of the acceptor it is designed to photosensitize, and the closer T_1 of donor and acceptor, the better. There are, of course, other requirements, but the energy relationships are critical.

4.84 PHYSICAL AND CHEMICAL PROPERTIES OF EXCITED STATES

We have touched briefly on the change in dipole moment upon excitation from a ground to an excited state, particularly in carbonyl compounds. Since dipole moments depend on the electron distribution in the molecule, knowledge of the occupied orbitals permits us to estimate dipole moments. In particular, knowledge of the orbitals from and to which an electron has been promoted allows us to estimate the difference between ground and excited state dipole moments. The former are readily measurable, but the excited state dipole moments are obtainable experimentally only indirectly and with great difficulty. These changes are frequently very large, as may be seen from Table 1.

* G. S. Hammond and N. J. Turro, *Science,* **142,** 154 (1963).

TABLE 1 Dipole Moments in Ground and Excited States[a]

Compound	Dipole Moment (Debye Units)	
	Ground	Excited
4-Amino-4'nitrobiphenyl	6.4	18
2-Amino-7-nitrofluorene	7	25
4-N,N-Dimethylamino-4'-nitrostilbene	7.6	32

[a] Taken in part from H. H. Jaffe and M. Orchin, *Theory and Applications of Ultraviolet Spectroscopy* (New York: John Wiley & Sons, 1962), p. 155.

Another physical property in which ground and excited states frequently differ is their geometry. Not only are bond distances and angles usually changed, but sometimes gross geometry may be different. Thus, planar formaldehyde, upon excitation, becomes pyramidal, and in planar ethylene, upon excitation, the two CH_2 groups become twisted by 90°.

A simple fundamental chemical property of many molecules is their acidity. Phenol, ⟨O⟩—ÖH, for example, in aqueous solution is a weak acid. Whereas aliphatic hydroxy compounds usually are barely acidic, the strong electronegative character of the aromatic carbon, the resonance stabilization and solvation of the anion, all account for the acidity of phenol. When this molecule is excited, it undergoes a $\pi \to \pi^*$ transition, and part of the lone pair π electron density on oxygen is promoted to an antibonding orbital which is principally on the ring system. (The excited state may be represented by ⟨⊖⟩=ÖH.) This promotion increases the positive character of the oxygen and should thus facilitate the departure of the proton — i.e., phenol should be a stronger acid in the excited state than in the ground state. On the other hand, consider the situation in a carboxylic acid such as benzoic acid ⟨O⟩—C⟨=O, OH⟩ . The $\pi \to \pi^*$ transition in this case transfers charge from the ring to the carbonyl group, represented by ⟨⊕⟩=C⟨O⁻, OH⟩ because the antibonding orbital is concentrated on this group. Accordingly, the acid strength is less in the excited than in the ground state. Table 2 shows some pK's of interest in these connections:

TABLE 2 *pK*'s of Some Molecules in the Ground (pK_G), Lowest Singlet (pK_S), and Lowest Triplet (pK_T) States[a]

Compound	pK_G	pK_S	pK_T
2-Naphthol	9.5	3.1	8.1
2-Naphthoic Acid	4.2	10–12	4.0
Acridine	3.7	10.6	5.6
Quinoline	5.5		6.0
2-Naphthylamine	5.1	−2.0	3.3
N,N-Dimethyl-1-Naphthylamine	4.9		2.7

[a] From Jaffe and Orchin, *op. cit.*, p. 156.

It will be noted that frequently the variation in acid strength is as much as a million-fold between the ground and first excited singlet state. In some molecules recently examined differences as large as 15 *pK* units have been observed. It is rather surprising that the *pK*'s of the lowest triplet seem to be close to those of the ground state; this is not completely understood at the present time.

5

The Hoffmann-Woodward Rules for Electrocyclic Reactions

5.1 ELECTROCYCLIC REACTIONS

Many reactions are known in which an acyclic π system such as butadiene is converted to a cyclic system by the formation of a single bond between the termini of the acyclic system:

The reverse ring opening reaction (i.e., the conversion of cyclobutene to butadiene) is also well known. Such transformations have been called electrocyclic reactions* because the closure or opening involves the movement of electrons and atoms — the formation of a σ bond from two previously π electrons — but no atoms are gained or lost.

---

* R. B. Woodward and R. Hoffmann, *J. Am. Chem. Soc.*, **87**, 395 (1965). Robert Woodward was born in 1917 in Boston, Massachusetts. He flunked out of Massachusetts Institute of Technology as an organic chemistry student in his sophomore year; given a second chance, he received his B.S. from the same Institution at 19 and by the age of 20, in 1937, had his Ph.D. Ever since he has been at Harvard University. He received the Nobel Prize in Chemistry in 1965. Roald Hoffmann was born in Poland in 1937 and became an American citizen in 1955. He received his undergraduate training at Columbia (B.A. in chemistry), his master's degree in physics in 1960, and his Ph.D. in chemical physics from Harvard in 1962. He is presently an Associate Professor of Chemistry at Cornell University.

74

5.2 CYCLOBUTENE ⇌ BUTADIENE INTERCONVERSIONS

5.21 THERMAL REACTIONS

It is known that heating dimethyl *cis*-1-cyclobutene-3,4-di-carboxylate* gives exclusively the dimethyl *cis,trans*-1,3-buta-diene-1,4-dicarboxylate. The reaction may be visualized as

cis   cis, trans (s − cis)   cis, trans (s − trans)

$$[Z = CO_2CH_3]$$

occurring by a rotation of the two $C \overset{Z}{\underset{H}{<}}$ groups. In order for the reaction to occur via the stereochemical path indicated, it is necessary that the rotations of the carbomethoxy groups proceed in the directions shown; in this case the rotations around the axes shown are in the same direction. In the rotational sense the two rotations conform; this process is called the conrotatory process. If the product had been the dimethyl *trans,trans*-1,3-butadiene-1,4-dicarboxylate, the two rotations would have had to occur in opposite directions:

cis   trans, trans (s − cis)   trans, trans (s − trans)

* See note, p. 93.

Or if the product had been the *cis,cis*-isomer, the rotations would also have had to occur in opposite directions:

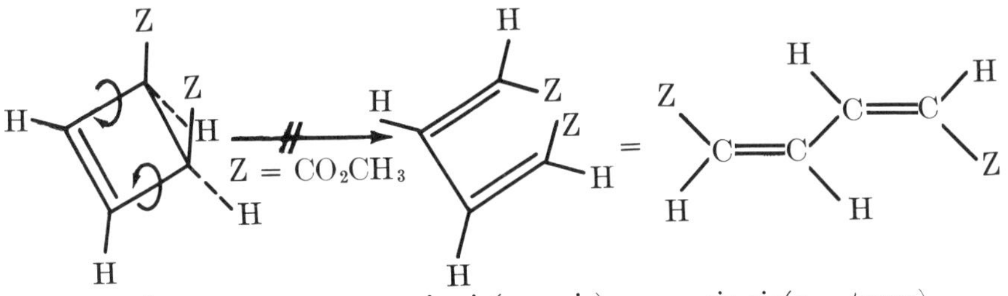

$Z = CO_2CH_3$

cis   cis,cis(s — cis)   cis,cis(s — trans)

In either case the rotations would have had to be opposite, or what is termed disrotatory. Since the product was *cis,trans* this particular electrocyclic reaction proceeds in the conrotatory fashion.

The conrotatory ring-opening also was shown to be controlling in the thermal conversion of tetramethylcyclobutenes. Thus the following stereospecific conversions occur:

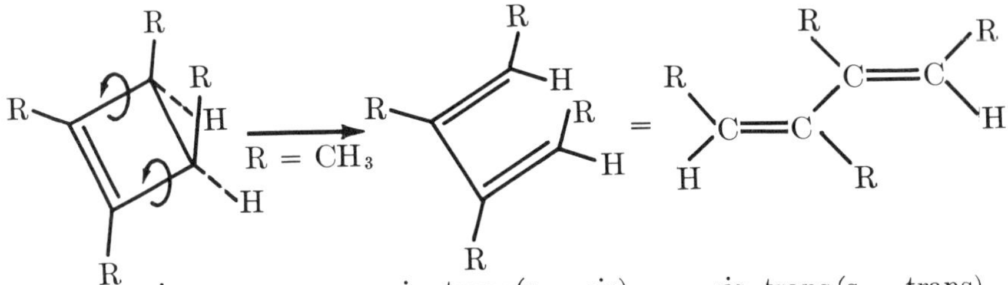

$R = CH_3$

cis   cis, trans (s — cis)   cis, trans (s — trans)

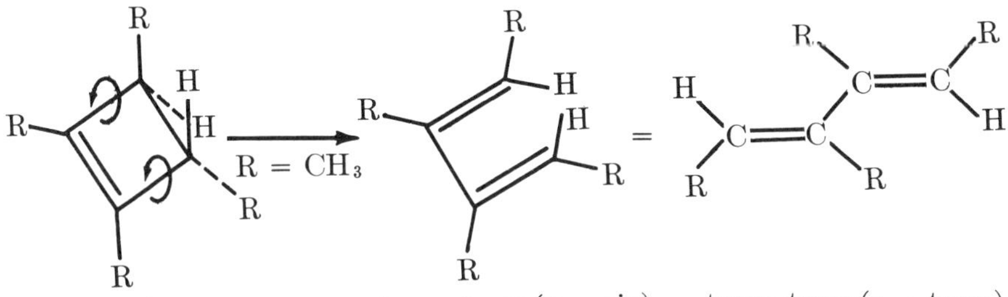

$R = CH_3$

trans   trans, trans (s — cis)   trans, trans (s — trans)

It has been suggested that the steric course of electrocyclic transformations is governed by the symmetry of the highest occupied molecular orbital of the acyclic partner. Let us examine the butadiene case more closely. In the molecular orbital treatment of the π system in butadiene, we generate four molecular orbitals from the four atomic pπ orbitals, one on each carbon atom. We can obtain a qualitative description of the molecular orbitals, focussing particularly on the nodes, lobe signs, and symmetry properties by recognizing that carbon atoms occur in equivalent pairs, 1 and 4, and 2 and 3. The four combinations are then made by adding and subtracting the sums and differences; i.e., $(1 \pm 4) \pm (2 \pm 3)$. Of the $2^3 = 8$ combinations, only four are possible, since the sign connecting C_1 and C_4 must be the same as that connecting C_2 and C_3. The results are shown in Fig. 5.1. In butadiene there are four pπ electrons and, in the ground state, these electrons occupy ψ_1 and ψ_2 to give the electron configuration $\psi_1{}^2\psi_2{}^2$. The highest occupied orbital in the ground state is thus ψ_2, and we wish to examine the symmetry of this orbital in more detail:

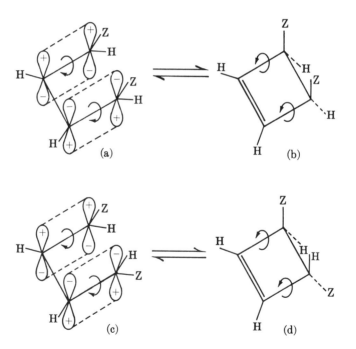

If we wish to involve a bonding interaction between the 1 and 4 carbon atoms (termini), it is apparent that only conrotatory motion of the termini around the bond axis will bring positive lobes of the orbitals of carbon atoms 1 and 4 into over-

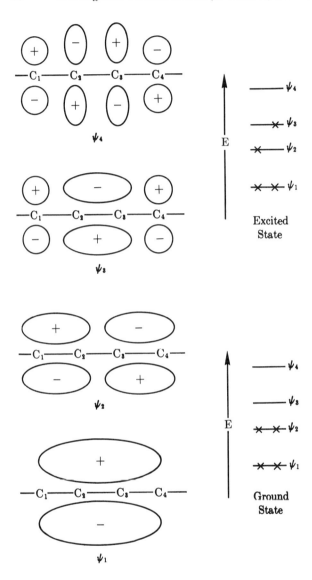

FIGURE 5.1 • The Four Molecular Orbitals of Butadiene.

lap. The conversion of the *cis* cyclic isomer (b) to the acyclic *cis,trans* isomer (a) (and *vice versa*) is consistent with this consideration. Furthermore, we can expect that the *trans*-cyclobutene (d) would be converted to the *trans-trans*-isomer (c) and *vice versa* because of the conrotatory process involved in the thermal or ground state interconversion of the butadiene-cyclobutene system.

5.22 PHOTOCHEMICAL INTERCONVERSIONS

Now let us turn our attention to the photochemical inter-conversion of cyclobutene and butadiene. In the first excited state of butadiene, an electron has been promoted from ψ_2 to the antibonding orbital ψ_3 (see Fig. 5.1), and the electronic con-figuration of this lowest energy excited state is $\psi_1^2\psi_2\psi_3$. We again examine the symmetry of the highest occupied MO which is now the antibonding orbital ψ_3:

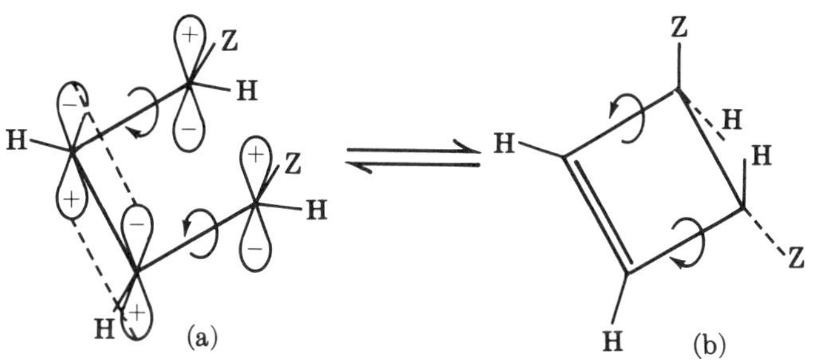

In order for the positive lobes of the orbitals on carbons 1 and 4 to overlap, it is now necessary that the rotations be disrotatory, with the stereochemical consequence that the ring-closing elec-trocyclic reaction of the *cis,trans* isomer (a) now leads to the *trans* isomer (b) (and *vice versa*). Thus we see that the photo-chemical (excited state) process proceeds in the disrotatory fashion; the thermal (ground state) process proceeds in the conrotatory fashion.

5.3 HEXATRIENE ⇌ CYCLOHEXADIENE INTERCONVERSIONS

Butadiene is a member of the $4n\pi$ electron system, i.e., a π electron system consisting of $4n$ electrons, where n is an integer which in this case is 1. The next member of the acyclic conju-gated polyene series is 1,3,5-hexatriene, the first member of the $4n + 2\pi$ electron system, with $n = 1$. Let us now examine the symmetry of the highest occupied orbital of this compound in order to determine the stereochemistry of the expected cyclized product, 1,3-cyclohexadiene, in both the thermal (ground state) and photochemical (excited state) conversion. The conclusions we draw will be again applicable to the reverse electrocyclic transformation; i.e., the ring opening of cyclo-hexadiene to hexatriene.

The combination of the six pπ atomic orbitals of hexatriene results in the six MO's shown in Fig. 5.2. These combinations result from the appropriate additions or subtractions of the equivalent sets: 1 and 6; 2 and 5; and 3 and 4; i.e., the MO's result from $(1 \pm 6) \pm (2 \pm 5) \pm (3 \pm 4)$. Theoretically one would obtain $2^5 = 32$ different possible combinations in which 1 is always positive. Of these combinations one set of six is the correct set. If $(1 + 6)$ is called A and $(1 - 6)$ is $(-A)$ and $(2 + 5)$ is B, $(2 - 5)$ is $(-B)$ and $(3 + 4)$ is C and $(3 - 4)$ is $(-C)$, then the proper combinations are:

$$(+A) + (+B) + (+C) : \psi_1 \quad (-A) + (-B) + (-C) : \psi_2$$

$$(+A) + (+B) - (+C) : \psi_3 \quad (-A) - (-B) - (-C) : \psi_4$$

$$(+A) - (+B) + (+C) : \psi_5 \quad (-A) - (-B) | (-C) : \psi_6$$

These combinations are not immediately obvious; in particular the combinations represented by ψ_4 and ψ_5; Fig. 5.2 would be difficult to develop. Fortunately, the proper wavefunctions for such linear conjugated polyenes can be developed by another and rather simple method, a method which gives the appropriate coefficients of the atomic orbitals in each molecular orbital. This method is the so-called "free electron method" or FEM. Although it is beyond the scope of this book to derive and develop the method, its application to hexatriene will be shown.

In the FEM it is assumed that the π electrons travel in a box of length a, assumed to be one bond length beyond each end of the conjugated system. Thus in hexatriene, the box is as-sumed to be $5 + 2 = 7$ bond lengths long. The FEM wave-functions for each of the six molecular orbitals is given by $\sin \dfrac{n\pi x}{a}$ where n is an integer, and x (a variable) is the distance traveled along the box by a π electron (measured in the same units as a). We are concerned with the value of ψ at various distances (x) along the length of the box, and in particular we wish to evaluate ψ at each carbon atom along the box or chain.

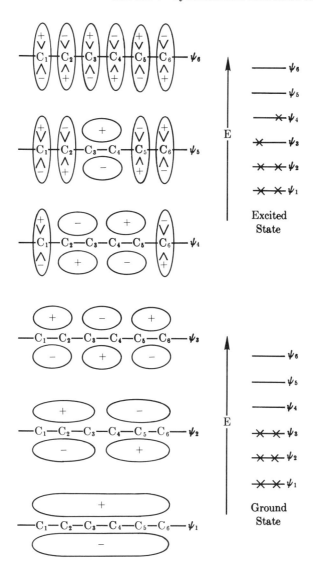

FIGURE 5.2 • The Six Molecular Orbitals of Hexatriene.

For $n = 0$, $\sin \dfrac{0\pi x}{a}$ vanishes everywhere and consequently is not an acceptable wavefunction. Thus the lowest energy wavefunction, ψ_1, has $n = 1$. From $x = 0$ to $x = a$, $\sin \dfrac{1\pi x}{a}$ goes from

0 through 1 to 0, always positive (cf. Fig. 5.3) and thus the wavefunction has no node. At carbon atom 1 the value of x/a is $1/7$ and hence the relative value of ψ is $\sin 1\pi/7 = \sin 25.7° = 0.43$, which is also the value of ψ at carbon 6 where $x/a = 6/7$. This value of ψ is equal (before normalization) to the coefficient c_{jr} (here c_{11} and c_{16}) occurring in the molecular orbital ψ_1 obtained by the lowest approximation of the Hückel method. The value of ψ_1 at carbon 2 is $\sin(1\pi 2/7) = \sin 51.4° = 0.78$; and at carbon 3 is $\sin(1\pi 3/7) = \sin 77.1° = 0.97$; the values at carbons 4 and 5 can be obtained in the same way.

In $\psi_2 = \sin\dfrac{2\pi x}{a}$, the value of $\dfrac{2x}{a}$ varies from 0 to 2 as x goes from 0 to a, hence the sin goes from 0 through 1 (at $\pi/2$), 0 (at π), and -1 (at $\pi/2$), to 0 (at 2π)(cf. Fig. 5.3), and thus we have a single node at $x/a = 3.5$. The value of $\sin\dfrac{2\pi x}{a}$ at carbon 1 ($x/a = 1/7$) is $\sin\dfrac{2\pi}{7} = 0.78$, and the value at carbon 6 is -0.78; at carbon 2, $\sin\dfrac{4\pi}{7} = 0.97$ and at carbon 5, $\psi_2 = -0.97$, etc. The wavefunctions (unnormalized) for the other molecular orbitals can be similarly determined, and these are shown in Fig. 5.3.

If attention is now directed to the thermal cyclization of hexatriene to cyclohexadiene, the orbital of interest is ψ_3, the highest occupied orbital in the ground state. It is seen from Fig. 5.2 that the 1 and 6 positions (the termini) in ψ_3 have lobes of the same sign on the same face, and thus the electrocyclic transformation, if it occurred, should be disrotatory; and in the case of a *trans,cis,cis*-isomer such as (a), the *trans* isomer (b) would result:

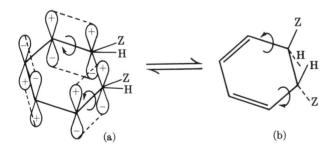

(a)   (b)

On the other hand, if we look at the highest occupied orbital in the first excited state of hexatriene (Fig. 5.2), the lobes at the termini have the same sign on opposite faces and now the cyclization should be conrotatory. We thus see that the situation with hexatriene $(4n + 2)$ is just opposite to that of butadiene $(4n)$; in the former, the thermal reaction should be disrotatory, the photochemical conrotatory, while with butadiene the reverse holds.

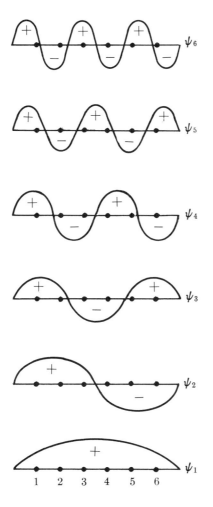

FIGURE 5.3 • FEM Representation of the Six MO's of Hexatriene.

5.4 REACTANT AND PRODUCT ORBITAL CORRELATIONS

It is instructive to examine the above electrocyclic transformations in greater detail, and for this purpose we shall again consider the conversion of cyclobutene to 1,3-butadiene. Such a conversion involves the net transformation of a σ bonding orbital to a π bonding orbital, and it is of crucial importance to correlate the sigma molecular orbital of the reactant (cyclobutene) with the appropriate molecular orbital of the product butadiene. In the starting material we have four molecular orbitals of interest: σ, σ^*, π, and π^*. The σ, σ^* orbitals are the bonding and antibonding orbitals of the 1,4-bond of cyclobutene (the bond to be broken), and the π and π^* orbitals refer to the 2,3-π bond (Fig. 5.4). The four molecular orbitals of the product are the familiar molecular orbitals of butadiene shown in Fig. 5.1. Each of the first set of orbitals passes into one of the second set, and we would now like to examine the way in which two sets of orbitals can be correlated.*

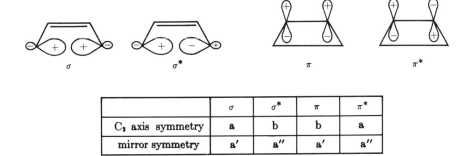

	σ	σ^*	π	π^*
C₂ axis symmetry	a	b	b	a
mirror symmetry	a′	a″	a′	a″

FIGURE 5.4 • The Orbitals of Cyclobutene and Their Symmetry.

The correlation depends upon whether the ring opening is conrotatory or disrotatory. Consider the conrotatory mode shown in Fig. 5.5a. In this mode, the system preserves a twofold (C_2) symmetry axis throughout the reaction, the axis in the plane of the molecule which bisects both the 2,3 and 1,4 bonds. Consider that each of the hydrogen atoms 1 to 4 move the same distance in the directions indicated. If we perform a 180° rotation around the symmetry axis (a C_2 operation),

---

* H. C. Longuet-Higgins and E. W. Abrahamson, *J. Am. Chem. Soc.* **87**, 2045 (1965).

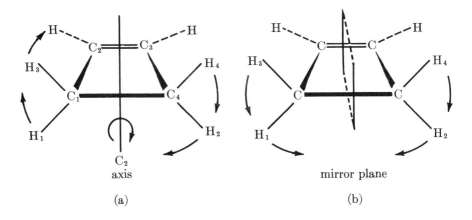

FIGURE 5.5 • Symmetries of (a) Conrotatory and (b) Disrotatory Modes.

then H_3 interchanges with H_2, H_1 with H_4, and the new configuration is indistinguishable from the original. With respect to this symmetry element, all orbitals transform into themselves or into minus themselves. In the former case we say the orbital is symmetric, called a, with respect to the C_2 operation, and the latter case antisymmetric, or b, with respect to C_2. In the case of the disrotatory ring opening, the system preserves not an axis of symmetry as in Fig. 5.5a but a plane of symmetry as in Fig. 5.5b. Consider that each of the hydrogen atoms 3 and 4 have moved the same distance in the direction indicated. If we reflect the molecule through a plane of symmetry perpendicular to the plane of the 4 carbons and bisecting the 2,3 and 1,4 carbon bonds, then H_3 interchanges with H_4, H_1 with H_2, and the new configuration is indistinguishable from the original. The orbitals involved will then be either symmetric (a') or antisymmetric (a'') with respect to the mirror plane.

We can now classify the orbitals of cyclobutene (Fig. 5.4) and those of *s-cis*-butadiene (Fig. 5.6) in each mode as follows:

TABLE 1   **Orbital Correlations for Cyclobutene $\rightleftharpoons$ Butadiene Interconversion.**

	Cyclobutene Orbitals	Butadiene Orbitals	Symmetry
Conrotatory Mode	$\begin{cases} \sigma, \pi^* \\ \pi, \sigma^* \end{cases}$	$\begin{cases} \psi_2, \psi_4 \\ \psi_1, \psi_3 \end{cases}$	$\begin{cases} a \\ b \end{cases}$
Disrotatory Mode	$\begin{cases} \sigma, \pi \\ \pi^*, \sigma^* \end{cases}$	$\begin{cases} \psi_1, \psi_3 \\ \psi_2, \psi_4 \end{cases}$	$\begin{cases} a' \\ a'' \end{cases}$

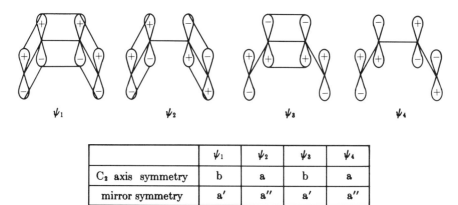

	ψ_1	ψ_2	ψ_3	ψ_4
C_2 axis symmetry	b	a	b	a
mirror symmetry	a′	a″	a′	a″

FIGURE 5.6 • The Orbitals of s-cis-Butadiene and Their Symmetries.

Now let us arrange the four orbitals of the cyclobutene and the four of the product butadiene in order of their relative energies. We expect σ orbitals to be the lowest and σ^* the highest energy orbitals, and π and π^* of intermediate energy, with π, of course, being more stable than π^*. The order of energy of the butadiene orbitals corresponds to the order of the number of nodes in the MO's with ψ_1 (no nodes)* being most stable and ψ_4 (three nodes)* least stable. Accordingly, we now have the orbital correlation shown in Fig. 5.7. It is thus seen that in the conrotatory mode,

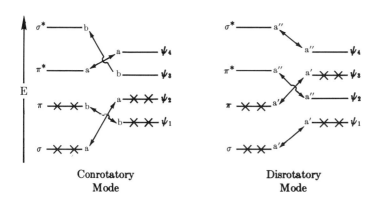

FIGURE 5.7 • Orbital Correlation for Cyclobutene ⇌ Butadiene.

the σ orbital of cyclobutene correlates with ψ_2 of butadiene and the π orbital with ψ_1, while in the disrotatory mode, σ of cyclobutene correlates with ψ_1 and π with ψ_3 of butadiene. The

---

* Other than the node coincident with the molecular plane.

ground state electronic configuration of cyclobutene is $\sigma^2\pi^2$; i.e., there are two electrons in each of the two lowest energy orbitals of interest. Now by the conrotatory process these electrons would end up in the lowest energy π orbitals of butadiene to give the configuration $\psi_1^2\psi_2^2$. It is therefore reasonable to conclude that energetically the conrotatory process would proceed readily. The reverse process, conversion of butadiene to cyclobutene, is also favored.

In the disrotatory mode, on the other hand, σ correlates with ψ_1, π with ψ_3, so that the butadiene formed would have the configuration $\psi_1^2\psi_3^2$ which is energetically highly unfavorable. For the reverse process, cyclization, the butadiene in the ground state $\psi_1^2\psi_2^2$ would go into the cyclobutene $\sigma^2\pi^{*2}$, again highly unfavorable.

5.5 SYMMETRY STATE CORRELATIONS

Writing the electronic configuration, such as that of the ground state of cyclobutene, in the form $\sigma^2\pi^2$, gives us information with respect to the particular orbitals occupied and the extent of their occupancy (the superscript). Instead of the orbital type notation, we may use the symmetry type of the orbital, which in this case is written a^2b^2. The total symmetry of the state (in this case, the ground state) may be obtained by treating the symmetry configuration, a^2b^2, as a mathematical product. We said above that a represented symmetric behavior and we can assign such behavior the mathematical symbol or character of $+1$. Then antisymmetric behavior has the character -1. If we make the substitutions in a^2b^2, we get $1^2(-1)^2 = 1$, which is totally symmetric, and we can now say the state belongs to the symmetric species and we give it the designation capital A. Returning to the correlation diagram of Fig. 5.7 we recall the conrotatory transformation of cyclobutene gave the configuration of $\psi_1^2\psi_2^2$ of butadiene or a^2b^2 and again A. Now let us consider the transformation of the first excited state of cyclobutene to excited butadiene. The first excited state of cyclobutene ($\sigma^2\pi\pi^*$) has the configuration $a^2ba = (1)^2(-1)(1) = -1$ which is antisymmetric and designated B; since σ correlates with ψ_2, π with ψ_1, and π^* with ψ_4, the $\sigma^2\pi\pi^*$ state correlates with $\psi_2^2\psi_1\psi_4 = a^2ba = B$ in butadiene. However, it will be noted that the butadiene configuration $\psi_1\psi_2^2\psi_4$ is not the lowest excited state of butadiene, which would

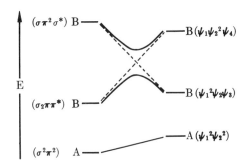

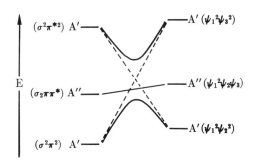

FIGURE 5.8 • State Correlation Diagram for Cyclobutene $\rightleftharpoons$ Butadiene. (a) Conrotatory Mode; (b) Disrotatory Mode.

be $\psi_1{}^2\psi_2\psi_3$, also $b^2ab = B$. Accordingly, the probability of cyclobutene in the lowest energy excited state $(\sigma^2\pi\pi^*)$ being transformed to butadiene in the correlated excited state $(\psi_1\psi_2{}^2\psi_4)$ is quite low because of the uphill energy requirement. A higher excited state of cyclobutene has the configuration $\sigma\pi^2\sigma^* = B$ corresponding to $\psi_1{}^2\psi_2\psi_3 = B$ of butadiene — its lowest possible energy excited state — and these two states are correlated. We can now draw a new correlation diagram in state notation for the conrotatory process (see Fig. 5.8a). By exactly the same kind of reasoning, we would arrive at the correlation diagram shown in Fig. 5.8b for the disrotatory process, assuming $+1$ for a', -1 for a''. The straight lines (either broken or full) connect the symmetry states that correlate with each other. However, because of the so-called non-crossing rule — electron repulsion prevents states of the same symmetry from crossing — the full lines represent the true correlations. Figure 5.8 shows that the thermal (ground state) conversion of cyclobutene to butadiene is energetically favorable for the conrotatory process, while the disrotatory process for the thermal conversion has an energy barrier (hump in the full correlation line). However, the conrotatory photochemical process from the first excited state of cyclobutene to the first excited state of butadiene has an energy barrier, while in the disrotatory mode there is no barrier.

The cyclobutene $\rightleftharpoons$ butadiene or hexatriene $\rightleftharpoons$ cyclohexadiene interconversions are examples of intramolecular electrocyclic reactions in which σ bond $\rightleftharpoons \pi$ bond interconversions occur. Such interconversions involve correlations of the orbitals of starting material and product with respect to either an axis or a plane of symmetry. If, in the correlation diagram, no bonding orbitals correlate with antibonding orbitals, then the thermal reaction is permitted. If, however, bonding orbitals of the reactant correlate with antibonding orbitals of the product, then the reaction is favored by the photochemical rather than the thermal process. In electrocyclic reactions generalized by the formula (Fig. 5.9) in which one π bond $\rightarrow$ one σ bond, if m (the number of π electrons) $= 4n + 2$ (where n is an integer, 0, 1, 2, 3, etc.), the electrocyclic reaction is thermally disrotatory if it proceeds, and photochemically conrotatory; however, for $m = 4n$, the process is thermally conrotatory and photochemically disrotatory, if it proceeds.

FIGURE 5.9 • Intramolecular Electrocyclic Reactions of System with $m \pi$ Electrons.

5.6 ETHYLENE DIMERIZATION

Rules for intermolecular cycloadditions have also been developed,* and the treatment for the ethylene-ethylene addition will be reproduced and elaborated for those with a deeper interest in such reactions.

The addition of two ethylene molecules to form cyclobutane probably involves a transition state in which the two ethylenes are in parallel planes directly above each other (Fig. 5.10). The four reactant π levels and the four corresponding σ levels in

* R. Hoffmann and R. B. Woodward, *J. Am. Chem. Soc.*, **87**, 2046 (1965).

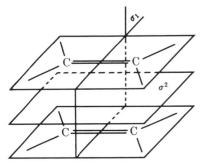

FIGURE 5.10 • Transition State for Ethylene Dimerization.

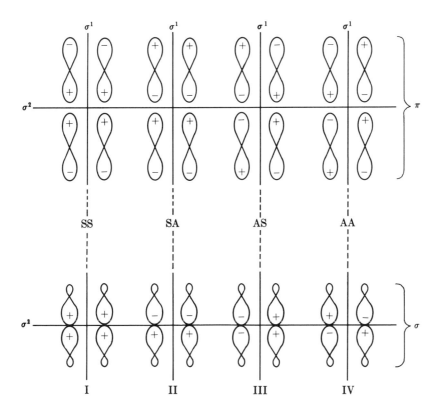

FIGURE 5.11 • Symmetries of Ethylene Orbitals Involved in Dimerization.

the product are classified as symmetric (S) or antisymmetric (A) with respect to σ_1, a plane bisecting the ethylenes, and σ_2, a plane parallel to and midway between the planes of the approaching molecules. The form of the molecular orbitals involved in the reaction, and all lying in the plane passing through the four carbon atoms, is shown in Fig. 5.11. The top half of Fig. 5.11 shows the four possible combinations of the π and π^* molecular orbitals of the two ethylene molecules. In combination I, upon approach of the two ethylene molecules, their bonding π molecular orbitals begin to overlap and a slight bonding contribution between the two ethylenes results because the overlap involves lobes of the same sign. We can call this combination π_1^+. In combination II, the same two bonding π molecular orbitals of the two ethylenes approach with lobes of opposite sign overlapping, leading to a slightly antibonding situation between the two ethylene molecules which we call π_1^-. Similarly in combinations III and IV, the antibonding π^* orbitals of the two ethylene molecules approach and begin to overlap to give again slightly bonding and slightly antibonding combinations III and IV, respectively, which we will call π_2^+ and π_2^-, respectively. The symmetries of these combinations, shown in Fig. 5.11 are: for π_1^+ symmetric (S) with respect to σ_1 and also symmetric (S) with respect to σ_2, hence abbreviated SS. Similarly π_1^- is SA, π_2^+ is AS and π_2^- is AA. In our notation, the subscript 1 in π_1^+ and π_1^- refers to a combination orbital of the transition state which is bonding within each ethylene; the subscript 2 in π_2^+ and π_2^- refers to antibonding character within the ethylenes. The superscript $+$ in π_1^+ and π_2^+ corresponds to incipient bonding between the two ethylenes; the minus in π_1^- and π_2^- refers to incipient antibonding between the two ethylenes.

In the lower half of Fig. 5.11 we have, according to the same symmetry scheme, similarly classified, in the product cyclobutane, the σ bonds between the carbons originating in different ethylenes. In these bonds, the principal energy contribution comes from the interaction of the two newly bonded carbons, so that combinations I and III are principally bonding, II and IV principally antibonding. A much smaller energy contribution comes from the interaction of those two new sigma bonds with each other, which is bonding for I and II and antibonding for III and IV. If we call the total combinations I, II, III, IV, σ_1, σ_2, σ_3, σ_4, respectively, we thus obtain the energy diagram shown in Fig. 5.12. The symmetry symbols a_1, a_2, b_1, b_2 indicate the different types of symmetry possible: $a_1(SS)$ totally symmetric; $b_1(SA)$ and $b_2(AS)$, antisymmetric with respect to σ_2

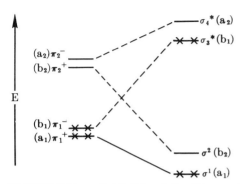

FIGURE 5.12 • Orbital Correlation Diagram for Ethylene Dimerization.

and σ_1, respectively; and $a_2(AA)$ antisymmetric with respect to both. The origin of these symmetry symbols and their use is beyond the scope of this book and may be found elsewhere.* However, to construct the state diagram we will need to know the products of these symmetry symbols. The necessary multiplications are: $a_2 b_1 = B_2$, $a_2 b_2 = B_1$, and $b_1 b_2 = A_2$, while multiplication by a_1 changes neither of the others, and each multiplied by itself gives A_1.

We now proceed to produce a state diagram. The ground state of the two ethylenes is $(\pi_1{}^+)^2(\pi_1{}^-)^2 = a_1{}^2 b_1{}^2 = A_1$. It correlates with $\sigma_1{}^2(\sigma_3{}^*)^2 = a_1{}^2 b_1{}^2 = A_1$, a doubly excited state of the cyclobutene. The ground state of cyclobutene, $\sigma_1{}^2 \sigma_2{}^2 = a_1{}^2 b_2{}^2 = A_1$ correlates with $(\pi_1{}^+)^2(\pi_2{}^+)^2 = A_1$, a doubly excited state of the ethylenes. This gives the now familiar pattern of correlation lines between states of equal symmetry trying to cross, repelling one another and giving an energy barrier. One of the first excited states of the two ethylenes, probably the lowest one in energy, is $(\pi_1{}^+)^2 \pi_1{}^- \pi_2{}^+ = a_1{}^2 b_1 b_2 = A_2$. This correlates with the cyclobutane state, which again is the lowest singly excited state, $\sigma_1{}^2 \sigma_2 \sigma_3^* = A_2$. We can now draw the state correlation diagram, as shown in Fig. 5.13. Thus it would appear that the photochemical reaction can occur, but the thermochemical reaction should not occur.

A further interesting feature is contained in this discussion. The transition state postulated for this photochemical reaction is a dimer formed from one ground state and one excited state molecule. Such dimers can be observed by spectroscopic means

* H. H. Jaffé and M. Orchin, *Symmetry in Chemistry* (New York: John Wiley and Sons, 1965).

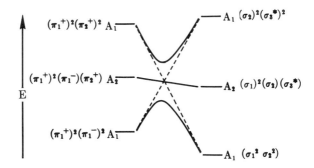

FIGURE 5.13 • State Correlation Diagram for Ethylene Dimerization.

and have been named *excimers* (excited state dimers). There are known to be at least two states of these, one higher and one lower in energy than the excited monomer.

We can again generalize the selection rules for the above reactions in which two π bonds lead to two σ bonds ($2\pi \rightleftharpoons 2\sigma$) (Fig. 5.14). Such a process will be allowed thermochemically for $m_1 + m_2 = 4n + 2$ (the Diels-Alder reaction between ethylene and butadiene) and photochemically for $m_1 + m_2 = 4n$ (the ethylene dimerization discussed above), where m_1 and m_2 are the number of π electrons in the two reacting fragments.

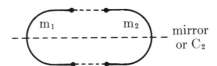

FIGURE 5.14 • Intermolecular Electrocyclic Reactions of the $2p\pi \rightarrow 2\sigma$ Type.

Note: A few words concerning *cis-trans* isomerism may be appropriate here. If one of the hydrogen atoms on each of the carbon atoms of ethylene is replaced by other atoms (either the same or different) two different compounds are possible. When these atoms (or the remaining H atoms) are on the same side of the carbon atoms, the compound is called *cis*; when on opposite sides, *trans*:

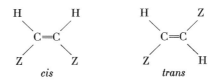

If two double bonds are present in a molecule, it is possible to have *cis-trans* isomerism around each double bond and hence four isomers are theoretically possible. Some confusion concerning the assignment of *cis* and *trans* configuration is sometimes possible. When multiple double bonds are present, it is the usual convention to assign the *cis* or *trans* configuration in relation to the skeletal or parent carbon chain. If the carbon chain connected by the double bond continues on the same side of a particular double bond, the configuration is *cis* at that double bond:

(a)

cis-2, *cis*-4

(b)

cis-2, *trans*-5

In these examples carbons 1 and 4 of (a) which are part of the parent carbon chain are on the same side (*cis*) of the C_2=C_3 double bond and carbons 3 and 6 which are also part of the parent carbon chain are both on the same side (*cis*) of the C_4=C_5 double bond. Hence this compound is *cis,cis*. The same reasoning leads to the *cis,trans* nomenclature for compound (b). This systematic naming scheme occasionally leads to unobvious conclusions. Consider for example the compound described as the *trans, trans, (s-trans)*-isomer on p. 76, where R = CH_3. The R's appear on the same side of each double bond and hence one might be tempted to conclude that this is the *cis,cis*-isomer. However applying the nomenclature rules, we see that the parent chain continues from both double bonds on the sides opposite to that of its origin and hence this isomer is correctly called 2,3-dimethyl-2-*trans*,3-*trans*-hexadiene.

In conjugated olefins there is some double bond character in the single bonds connecting the vinyl groups. This partial double bond character leads to a rotational barrier around such single bonds; hence, in a diene two conformational isomers are theoretically possible. When the two vinyl groups are on the same side of the single bond, the isomer is *s*-cis; when on opposite side, *s*-trans:

s — cis

s — trans

Here the *s* stands for the configuration around the single bond. Thus in a conjugated diene it is not only possible to have *cis* and *trans* isomers around each of the double bonds, but it is also possible to have *s-cis* and *s-trans* configurations around the single bond. Whether such *s* isomers can, in fact, be isolated depends on the energy barrier to rotation. This barrier is most frequently sufficiently small that at room temperature there is rapid equilibration and thus the *s-trans* isomer with its smaller steric requirements is the predominant isomer. When, in the conjugated diene described above, one of the H atoms at each end of the chain is replaced by the same group, then *cis,trans* and *trans,cis* isomers are identical and only the following six isomers are possible:

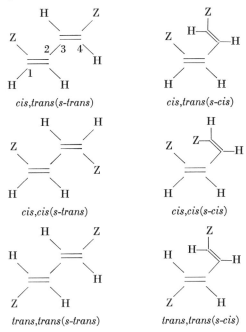

cis,trans(s-trans)	*cis,trans(s-cis)*
cis,cis(s-trans)	*cis,cis(s-cis)*
trans,trans(s-trans)	*trans,trans(s-cis)*

If Z ≠ Z in the above example, then the *cis,trans* and *trans,cis* isomers would not be identical and since each of them could exist as *s-cis* and *s-trans* there would be a total of $2^3 = 8$ isomers possible.